# HERBS

## The Magic Healers

### PAUL TWITCHELL

# HERBS:
# THE MAGIC HEALERS

Copyright © 1971 by ECKANKAR
ISBN: 0-914766-10-4

This book does not propose to replace the services of anyone's family physician, who should be consulted for conditions requiring his services.

9th Printing—1982

Cover design by Stan Burgess

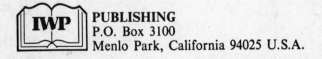

**PUBLISHING**
P.O. Box 3100
Menlo Park, California 94025 U.S.A.

# TABLE OF CONTENTS

# Chapter One

## HERBS, THE ANCIENT WAY TO PHYSICAL AND SPIRITUAL WELL-BEING

The spiritual healing work in ECKANKAR, the Ancient Science of Soul Travel, is done by the hoary method of *Atma* (Soul) out-of-the-body movement. Healing is but one aspect of ECKANKAR. Its primary purpose is to give Soul an opportunity to travel the ancient, secret path to the realm of God where it becomes a co-worker with the SUGMAD, the Supreme Deity.

However, the ancient formulas of herbs, spices, and minerals are still available. That is why this book on herbs is being made available today, so that all who do not have any contact with the Living ECK Master or other Masters can have the opportunity to find release from physical and mental health problems.

For thousands of years herbs have been used by the adepts of the ancient order of the Vairagi, the Masters of ECKANKAR, to correct the spiritual and physical conditions of their chelas.

During the ancient times, these adepts taught their chelas where to find the proper herbs and how to use them to soothe the anguish of body and heart. These herbs brought about "magical" changes in the individual who needed a singular ingredient to bring him back to well-being again.

The ECK Master does not lean upon herbs to make the adjustment from illness to the complete man again; he works with the individual according to his level of spiritual unfolding. If one has developed far enough up the spiritual ladder of God, it requires little effort to heal the psychic wounds or illness of the physical self.

Modern medicine is founded upon herbs, plants, flowers, minerals, and spices. We know through the study of herbs that new ingredients for the healing of man's mind and body are being found in jungles of South America and other parts of the world. The ECK Master is gradually leading man to the places where herbs grow wild in order to help raise bodily health conditions. Every ECK Master follows the old axiom in ECKANKAR: "It is better to have a healthy body when trying to reach God-Realization than one filled with pain, anguish, and sickness." It is taught that one concentrates better upon God or any subjective experience in life with a healthy mind and body.

The ECK Master also teaches that what is good for one individual in herb healing may not be especially so with another; everyone cannot use the same herbs for the same results. Everyone is different in his consciousness and in his body metabolism. Therefore, he must accept the fact that whatever one person can use and benefit from may not be best for himself. Generally speaking, one formula for an herb mixture produces a remedy for numerous people; but in the long run, there is no sure single prescription for everyone. If a person needs a diagnosis or a prescription for a specific health problem, he should see his own physician, who can handle his case according to the laws of medicine.

Aristotle, the great Greek philosopher, left a book, *Golden Cabinet of Secrets*, which was composed of many formulas, recipes, and prescriptions regarding certain herbs and plants that he and his contemporaries had studied. He found many plants to be poisonous and narcotic in nature, so his works were kept secret. Certain highly influential politicians of his time would not have hesitated to use such herbs and plants for the degradation of many of the people, so Aristotle passed the information on only to the more trustworthy of his followers.

Aristotle discovered herbs that were astringents and had the property of contracting tissue. He also found the antispasmodics, which helped prevent spasms and relieved muscular irritability. He found demulcents, which soothed the membranes of the nose and throat, helping coughs and colds.

The philosopher wrote voluminously about tonics, sedatives, aromatics, laxatives, and purgatives. Many famous people of history used the recipes which Aristotle put together, including Alexander the Great and Cleopatra.

The magic of herbs wove its spell over the people of the Middle Ages. The witches were the greatest advocates of herbal medicines and magic. Satan, the Prince of Darkness, was supposed to possess mysterious powers gained from a concoction he brewed during those Dark Ages. He has apparently retired from this area of influence and now works spells with the Kal (negative) power over the hearts and minds of the people in modern times.

The peoples of the Middle Ages believed there was magic in the herbal philtres. Herbs and plants were the basis of the love potions and aphrodisiacs. These potions were used in every way—sometimes given as a liquid to drink and at other times poured over various parts of the body; for example, on the soles of the feet.

The ancient writings of Aristotle, Democritus, Paracelsus, Albertus Magnus and others included many recipes for love powders and philtres. During the time of Queen Elizabeth, the roots of the eryngo, the sea holly, were used for a love tonic. During the Renaissance love potions made from herbs became a thriving business.

Percy Shelley, the great English poet, used many

herbal concoctions during his search for eternal youth in Italy. He often mixed his own herbs in order to develop the right recipe to make himself youthful. Lord Byron, his companion in Italy, helped in the search, but neither seemed to have found the secret recipe for physical immortality, as both died quite young. Shelley died by drowning, Byron by malaria.

Wandering tribes were most knowledgeable in herbs as they depended upon them for survival. The wisdom of plant lore was handed down through the ages from generation to generation. It was especially true of the tribes in the Far East, mostly those in China where the mandrake and ginseng root still hold great value.

Common sense tells us that nature supplies most of our foods from the vegetable and herb kingdom; therefore, we know it supplies the remedies for most illnesses. Every animal has an inborn instinct, and when sick, will seek out certain grasses, weeds, or plants to eat. We owe a great deal to the American Indians and natives of other countries, who during the centuries, have taught man how to cure his ailments with herbs. Science now confirms through chemical analysis the fact that all chemical elements of which our body is composed are also found in the roots, barks, leaves, flowers, and fruits of herbs.

We have also learned that each family of plants and herbs has its own peculiar ability for extracting from the earth a specific group of mineral elements. The lime plants, which are the legumes, peas, beans, clovers, etc., supply calcium, potassium, phosphorous, and similar minerals which are the materials to build bones, ligaments, and teeth. The lily family stores organic sulphur; the iron plants supply food for the blood; and the phosphorous plants supply food for the brain and the nervous system.

Within the herb kingdom we find not only food materials, but tonics, laxatives, astringents,

8

stimulants, sedatives, and every element needed to balance the body chemistry, to overcome body ills, and to bring about health.

The following list gives many herbs according to their need and properties for the body. This is not a complete list because space does not allow it.

*The Amulet Herbs.* These are used by many people who believe in their occult value to bring "good luck." Some of these herbs have medicinal properties, but they are used primarily because of their alleged benefit to the seeker of good fortune. Often the herbs are sewed into a bag and carried around the neck. Some people merely place a bag of these herbs in their purse or carry them in a pocket somewhere on their person.

These herbs are as follows: The Adam and Eve Root, Alkanet Root, Betel Nut, Buckeye, Cumin Seed, Devil Shoe String, Five Finger Grass, Grains of Paradise, High John the Conqueror, Holy Herb, Holy Sandalwood, Jezebel Root, Lesser Periwinkle, Life Everlasting, Lovage Root, Queen's Root, Sacred Bark, Sea Spirit, Southern John the Conqueror, Sumbul Root, Tonka Beans, and Wahoo Bark.

*The Anthelmintic Herbs.* It is said these herbs rid the body of tapeworms and other types of parasitic worms in the stomach and intestines. This type of complaint is common among those, who in their search for independence, become unkempt and neglectful of body sanitation. It is also common among young people, especially those who surf and go barefooted much of the time in warm climates such as Florida, California, and Southwest and southern United States. Parasitic worms constitute a problem in India where it is a necessity to go without shoes, especially among the religious there. Most so-called holy men and religious seekers in India are bothered by worms because of a lack of body sanitation.

While on this point, it is well to inform those who

9

always believe what is being taught in the Orient as Truth in religious and spiritual matters of the conditions in ashrams and monasteries. These ingenious people would be startled to know that most of these places are filled with disease and sex perversions. Few ashrams in the Orient are kept up to the standards of Western sanitation. As a result, the occupants live in filth and disease. Many of the young priests are taught to be celibates, but there is nothing said about self-abuse.

The herbs in the Anthelmintic category are as follows: Elm Bark, Flax Seed, Malefern, Pomegranate, Pumpkin Seed, and Wormwood.

*The Aromatic or Carminative Herbs.* These are generally pleasant and pungent to the taste. They are often used to make other drugs more palatable and to prevent griping pain in cathartics. Their use is to rid the body of stomach and intestinal gases.

These herbs are as follows: Angelica Root, Anise Root, Canada Snake Root, Caraway, Cardamon Seed, Catnip Herb, Celery Seed, Coriander Seed, Cumin Seed, Elecampane Root, Parsley Root, Peppermint, Sassafras Bark, Spearmint, Sweet Clover, Wild Ginger and Yarrow Herb.

Mixed with a meal these often prevent gases arising in the stomach and intestines. The ECK Master has long used these for the purpose of good digestion and has recommended them to the chelas of the true spiritual works. They help to keep the body in good health and are part of the botanicals used in our daily lives.

*The Astringent Herbs.* These are herbs used for botanical formulas to contract the tissues of the body when the physician deems it necessary.

They are as follows: Alum Root, Bilberry, Black Alder Bark, Blackberry Bark, Black Cherry, Black Willow, Butternut Bark, Gold Thread, Hawthorn Fern, Iron Wood, Kola Nuts, Life Everlasting, Maidenhair Fern, Mountain Ash Bark, Water Lily

Root, White Oak Root, Sweet Fern Root, and Swamp Snake Root.

*The Herbs Used in Dyes and Coloring.* These herbs were first used by the primitive Indian tribes in North America for dyeing clothes and coloring headdresses. Later they were put to use in the cosmetic industry for toilet preparations, hair tonics, and dyes in clothing plants and shops where dresses and men's clothes are assembled for retail sales.

These herbs and the colors they produce are as follows: Alkanet—red; Black Malva—black; Blood Root—red; Blue Malva—blue; Henna Leaves—yellow; Golden Seal—yellow; Madder—red; Sage—green; Saffron—red; Sumach Leaves—brown; Red Saunders—red; and Walnut Hulls—brown.

You can see that it was relatively easy for the primitive tribesman to find colors in the herbs of the fields and forest whenever he wanted to dye any of his clothing and other daily wares such as arrows, weapons, or feathers.

*The Diuretic Herbs.* These are used in medicines to flush the kidneys and promote the secretion of urine. Generally, they are used when the kidneys are not active enough.

These herbs are as follows: Beth Root, Birch Leaves, Burdock Seeds, Corn Silk, Dog Grass, Dwarf Elder Bark, Horseradish Root, Indian Chickweed, Juniper Berries, Kava Kava, Parsley Root, Pimpernel, Pipsissewa, Seven Barks, Skunk Cabbage, Sweet Bugle, Trailing Arbutus and Watermelon Seed.

The problem here is that most people have a tendency to use diuretics to an excess, thus overstimulating the kidneys.

*The Expectorants.* These herbs tend to modify the quality and quantity of the mucous secretions and favor its expulsions in case of colds and coughs and irritations of the throat.

The Expectorant herbs are as follows: Balm of Gilead Buds, Butterfly Weed, Hoarhound, Life

Everlasting, Nettle Leaves, Seneca Root, Solomon Seal, Wahoo Bark, Wild Cherry Bark and White Pine Bark.

These are the chief ingredients used in medicines for colds and coughs. They were first used by the medicine man in the primitive tribes, especially the American Indians. They were found in the medicine chests of the early settlers in this country.

*The Fragrant Herbs.* The fragrant botanicals are used in sachet perfumes, incense mixtures, and in the manufacture of certain flavors. The ancient Persians and Greeks were heavy users of these herbs, as were the Chinese.

They are as follows: Cassia Bark, Cloves, Deer Tongue, Gum Myrrh, Lavender Flowers, Master of the Wood, Orris Root, Penny Royal, Peppermint, Sandalwood, Rose Petals, Tansy Herb, Tonka Bean, Wild Ginger, Wild Vanilla, and Wintergreen.

*The Laxative Herbs.* These are the herbs which stimulate the secretions of the intestinal glands and excite the movement of the bowels. They are the basis for the patent medicines found so commonly on the drug shelves today, known simply as laxatives.

The laxative herbs are as follows: Blue Gentian, Black Butternut, Cascara, Dandelion Root, Flax Seed, Golden Seal, Licorice Root, May Wort, Rhubarb, Senna Pod, Snakehead, St. John's Bread, Tulip Tree, Turtlebloom, and Yellow Root.

*The Nervine Herbs.* They are the basis for the patent medicines that can be bought in any drugstore for mild nerve disorders. They have a soothing influence on nerves which have been subjected to unnecessary excitement and strain.

These herbs are as follows: Blue Scull Cap, Blue Vervain, Celery Seed, Fragrant Valerian, Hop Flower, Kola Nuts, Lady Slipper, Mistletoe, Mugwort, Musk Root, Rosemary, Sweet Basil, and Wild Lettuce.

*The Purgative Herbs.* These are similar to the laxatives, except they are far stronger and induce a much heavier action on the bowels. They are also found to form a base for patent medicines sold at the drug counter.

These herbs are as follows: Black Root, Boneset Herb, Buckthorn Bark, Mandrake Rhizome, May Apple Root, and Senna Leaves.

*The Tonic Herbs.* They are divided into two parts: Those called simply tonics and used primarily by women for their particular needs. Secondly, those called stomachics which promote nutrition and tone up the stomach for loss of appetite.

The tonic herbs are as follows: Alder, Angelica Root, Bearberry, Beth Root, Blue Cohosh, Elecampane Root, Life Root, Lovage, Pale Cohosh, Palmetto Berries, Queen's Delight, Papoose Root, Rosemary, Shepherd's Purse, Squaw Root, Squaw Vine, and Tansy.

The stomachic herbs are as follows: Angelica Root, Blackberry Root, Blue Gentian, Chicory Root, Chocolate Root, Columbo, Congo Root, Dandelion Root, Elecampane, Ginseng Root, Golden Seal, Jamaica Ginger, Juniper Berries, Mugwort, Quassia, Solomon Seal, Thyme, Waywort, Wild Cherry Bark, Wild Sage, Wild Sarsaparilla, and Wild Strawberry.

The herbs so named are part of those which make up the botanicals. These are the plants, flowers, and herbs that are used in medical prescriptions and patent medicines. But we must remember that much of the real value of herbs has been lost through the centuries from ancient times because many have become domesticated garden types.

Six to ten thousand years ago all living things in the fields and woods contained abnormal carbon, which is radioactive and breaks down so half of it becomes normal carbon six thousand or more years later.

Agriculture began in the ancient East in the region of Anatolia, Syria and Mesopotamia. In the Western world it began in Mexico. In both of these regions it

13

started near the end of the last ice age, about 7000 B.C. In both regions it began with the cultivation of plants and extended later to the herding of animals.

What does all this add up to? Because of a lack of the proper carbon in the plants, flowers, and herbs today, we are resorting to artificial means of assisting the body in its struggle in this earth world.

The development of man from the Neolithic era to the present day could be viewed through the history of plants. Plants certainly must have had an influence upon the chromosomes in man.

During the latter years and into the modern age, something has happened and it must be the chemical laboratory that has brought about changes in modern man.

Wild grain in ancient times gave a high yielding bread wheat that contained more of the body-feeding ingredients than today. It certainly had more normal carbon than in modern foods. We find that some grains, herbs, and plants grow better in certain farming areas. For example, rye grows better in the highlands rather than in ground at a low level. Wild rice in lowlands had a richer quality than in the highlands.

The interbreeding of races also brought about changes in the cultivation of grain and other products. It meant changes in locations as tribes moved to other places. About five thousand years ago as the farmers spread into new lands, met the hunters and produced new families of hunters, farmers, and herders, the movements into Europe and Egypt called for adaptations of crops, stock, and people. The new breed of agriculturists brought with them new ideas and methods which in turn affected the carbon content in the field and farm products. The grains, plants, herbs, and flowers, the botanicals which were the ancestors of the ingredients used in modern medicines, began to lose their natural properties. Today, they do not possess the same powerful ingredients.

14

The pedigree stock of herbs was lost in the transaction of crossbreeding and transplanting from different areas. These plants have been so robbed of their natural properties that little has been left for stability in the ingredients being used today. The reason for this is that we find few herbs growing wild in countries maintaining a high civilization.

We do find natural herbs in the South American jungles and in Africa. Many grow in the highlands of China, and of course, they can be picked wild on the slopes of the Himalayan foothills in Northern India and in Tibet. There are herb hunters just as there are orchid seekers, both braving the jungles for their precious botanical quarry.

This evolution of plants was given little thought by the scientists and rarely by the average man. But at the same time, we must realize there is a reincarnation and Karmic pattern of life going on here, similar to that of the Soul which inhabits the human body. A plant has a consciousness, even though it only expresses itself in one dimension, whereas man expresses himself in several ways.

We find that plants respond to the calendar seasons, as does man. Man is subject to the seasonal consumption of plants, or he must provide some method by which they can be dried, preserved, or kept stored safely in order to be consumed during an off-season period.

Today we get too many artificial products made in the laboratories or too many foods handled in the canning industries with preservatives detrimental to the health of man. In addition man is not free from the poisonous effects of the sprays he used to rid his crops of insects.

We have those who say that if we think right and hold good thoughts, nothing can harm us, we will have good health. This is not always true because we are dealing with bacteria which have a destroying power if we do not have healthy enough bodies to counteract the attack upon bodily tissue.

Throughout the ages, man has been far more interested in herbs possessing magic ingredients which would give him a great love attraction or bring him good fortune. He seldom connected the herb with his health. Only a few informed people, the medicine man, witch, alchemist, apothecary, monk, and philosopher had the knowledge to make use of the herbs and plants, and they commonly put some religious qualification upon the herb, rather than use it for beneficial health reasons.

There were many who used mixtures of herbs to be toted on their person. At first these were carried in a small bag around the neck. Later, herbs were put into a jeweled receptacle which took the form of a heart and was called an amulet of love.

Sandalwood mixed with rose water is still used in some parts of India during the middle of April by women who sprinkle the mixture on all they meet. This symbolizes the washing away of the impurities of the old year and the starting of the new year without sin.

The herbs are mentioned several times in the various sacred religious writings of the worlds. We also find that they are given space in the *Shariyat-Ki-Sugmad*, the holy writings of ECKANKAR. Prominent is the Balm of Gilead, a small shrub, native to the Middle Eastern countries.

This herb is found in the mountains of Gilead east of the Holy Land. It is found among the fragrant shrubs and called Amyria, a small tree, which yields the celebrated balm. It is a resinous substance obtained by making incisions in the tree. When first tapped the substance is white, but once exposed to air, it turns a golden color and looks much like honey.

The bud of the tree is a botanical which is used as part of a medicinal remedy for disorders of the lungs, stomach, and kidneys. The buds are also made into an ointment for rheumatic and gouty pains.

It is said that the base of the famous Tiger Balm made in Hong Kong is from this herb. Tiger Balm has met with much success throughout all Asia and the Far East.

In ancient times there was a legend of magical significance attached to the Balm of Gilead. It was thought to be so potent that if a person coated his hands with it he could hold them over fire without harm.

So many of the negative emotions can be handled by anyone in good health. Many people do not understand that health is the first factor on the road to God-Realization. If one is in good health, one is better able to do spiritual exercises than if one suffers from pain and anguish.

Half the curatives on the drug counters today are not directly from the herbs of the fields, mountains, and woods, but from the test tube. The trouble here is that few of these artificial nostrums have the full curative powers for the diseases which attack modern man today.

In the herb kingdom we find the most remarkable combinations of elements which suit every requirement of the human system. Just why the researchers for the chemical laboratories do not turn more fully to herbs, plants, flowers, and similar things is puzzling. Not only do herbs supply food materials, but tonics, laxatives, astringents, stimulants, sedatives, diuretics, stone dissolvers, and every element needed to balance the body chemistry and overcome disease.

A lifetime is required to learn the names, nature, and habits of the hundreds of thousands of plants that compose the herb kingdom. It would also take several thousand years to learn the medicinal or the therapeutic nature of a comparatively small number of them. But the future holds promise that within the next fifty years we shall double or triple the national knowledge of herbs. Thus we shall help resolve the problems of disease and considerably lengthen the span of life on earth.

The ECK Masters have realized that it is not the knowledge of a large number of herbs that brings the greatest botanical benefit for people, but the thorough knowledge of a few of the better ones. Thorough knowledge includes just how herbs should be prepared, blended, and mixed so that they are compatible with one another and augment one another to keep from reducing individual effectiveness.

One learns not to blend certain incompatible herbs. For example, Yellow Dock Root, a blood tonic, would not be mixed with Oak Bark, because the tannic acid in the latter and iron in the former are incompatible with one another. Tannic acid united with iron forms tannate of iron which produces intestinal disorders and constipation.

The principal abuses in eating are the consumption of excessive amounts of starch and glutinous foods—too much bread, cooked cereals, potatoes, macaroni, spaghetti, all beans (except string beans), peas, lentils, pies, cakes, pastry, blancmange, thick soups, gravies, chocolate milks and foods of similar nature.

If eaten in excess these mucous and acid-forming foods do not perfectly digest and they will ferment in the digestive tract, forming alcohol and acetic acid. They tend to clog the mucous membranes and produce catarrhs, colds, and bowel troubles.

One of the points which the ECK Masters tried to get across to the ECK chelas during ancient times was that calcium chloride is a great nutrient for the heart. Medical support for such an assertion was discovered several years ago by medical scientists in England. An herb containing calcium chloride, such as Motherwort, may help avert heart failure. By some mysterious process this herb is able to draw the green chloride out of the soil and convert it into calcium chloride in an organic nontoxic form. Water soluble, it will easily enter the blood on digestion in the stomach and find its way to the heart muscles and other tissues where it replenishes lost energy expended in the staggering amount of work performed by the heart. It is said that the heart consumes enormous amounts of calcium chloride.

There are several herbal heart remedies, each seemingly designed for some specific condition of the heart. The family of lime plants which helps the heart so much seems to be able to take advantage of certain waste elements and convert them into nourishing foods.

Another herb used in the treatment of heart trouble is the Hawthorn Apple. Formerly regarded sacred (traditionally it furnished Jesus' crown of thorns) it was chosen by Henry VII of England as part of his coat of arms. The Hawthorn Apple is called *Crataegus oxyacantha* from the Greek word meaning hard, sharp, wood thorn.

The Hawthorn tree grows to a height of about thirty feet and lives to an old age. It produces a fruit, a miniature apple, which when ripe is a brilliant red. Hence, the Hawthorn Apple. It is sometimes known as a berry and is also used as a diuretic, as an astringent, and as a tonic for sore throats.

Chapter Two

# THE RESTORATION
# OF SPIRITUAL HEALTH
# THROUGH HERBS

The restoration of spiritual health through herbs should be a goal of every individual in his life.

By speaking of the spiritual health of man I do not talk about body tissue or the things that go to make up only the physical well-being of the individual. I speak of the mental and the emotional, which are the elements that make up the psychic and Soul Faculties of man.

Once we have established good health in these areas, the physical aspect of man is bound to improve and bloom in exceedingly wondrous ways.

It is in these inner planes of man that many are able to find themselves advancing rapidly on the path to spiritual unfoldment, and eventually, God-Realization. Man first becomes aware of himself, which is Self-Realization, then gains knowledge of Soul, and later God-Realization, which is the knowledge of God. The use of the proper foods and herbs will assist in the spiritual unfoldment of every individual.

In the East, herbal treatment is known to have become well patronized long before the era of Hippocrates. The *Pen Tsao*, the great herbal book of China, was in use about three thousand years before the beginning of Christianity. Probably one of the oldest books on medical remedies, it went into much detail about the use of herbal medicines.

Another manuscript, perhaps older than the *Pen Tsao*, was the *Ebers Papyrus*, dating from 1500 B.C., which lists over eight hundred herbal remedies, including castor oil. Parts of the *Shariyat-Ki-Sugmad*, the original sacred writings of ECKANKAR, include discussions of many herbs, plants, and flowers. Pliny states in his *Natural History* that he believed there was an herbal remedy for every physical disorder.

The herbalists have never claimed that their herb could cure in the same sense that antibiotics or allopathics do, by killing germs or destroying toxic poisons in the body. All the herb, or its distilled essence, can do is assist the body by stimulating its resistance to attacks upon its tissues.

With allopathic medicine there is a need to produce results quickly. The allopathic medicines depend on the herbs to stimulate the life force, but regardless of this, herbalism continues to lose ground. Today, we find that herbalism has ceased to be an effective branch of medicine, except perhaps, in the field of patent medicines.

However, we are finding some attempt to revive herbalism. Certain writers, lecturers, and maverick practitioners of unorthodox medicines are trying to put herbs to an effective use once more. Unless something is done soon, true herbalism will, like many branches of fringe medicines, be lost.

Interwoven with the legends and myths of time and history is the truth about herbs. For example, we have the account of the mysterious manna which fell from heaven for the wandering Israelites as they fled from the Egyptians. In truth this was an herbal agent which was the product of the Tamarisk, a tree that gives off a juice through its bark. It is valued as a healing herb, but because of its agreeable taste it was considered food from heaven by the wandering tribe of Moses. Another "manna" which they found and ate was the Coriander Seed.

Herbs like Spikenard, Frankincense, and Myrrh

were generally used in ancient times as incense with the special property of centering the mind on devotion and producing an elevated mental state. Such a heightened state of consciousness in turn affects the psychic senses and increases the phenomena of psychic awareness.

Myrrh is that herb given to arouse the spiritual senses in man. It is probably valued above all other herbs as an incense ingredient. It was, in ancient times, mixed with benzoin. The ECK Masters have used it at times to help a chela become spiritually aroused so that he can gain some experience of survival through Soul Travel. This is not a general practice, however, for the ECK Masters of the ancient Order of the Vairagis want the chela to learn Soul Travel by his own conscious volition, and not by having to lean upon something like Myrrh or other props to get out of his physical senses into the spiritual worlds.

Hyssop is another herb which was, and still is, used in the religious worlds. It was mainly used in the early days as a symbol of purification. Later it was discovered to be valuable as a healing agent for wounds of warriors wounded in battle or injured in accidents.

The wound was dressed with Hyssop leaves as a protection against infection and to promote healing. This was done in the beginning with a crude effectiveness, but then the physicians and nurses became more proficient. This herb was the object of much superstition until modern medical researchers found that the mold which grows on the Hyssop leaves produced penicillin.

Today we have some 350,000 known herbs and plants which have been examined and classified. It is said that approximately 4,000 new species are added to the list yearly. Yet man is still lacking in the knowledge of what the totality of these herbs and plants might be in maintaining the health of the individual.

Nearly twenty-five million dollars are spent yearly trying to learn new data on plants and herbs. Perhaps there exists an herbal remedy for every disease if the truth could be learned about the vast amount of herbs in this world.

One herb, which has never become too popular with the general public, except for the Italians, is common garlic. For over five thousand years it has been used to cure many ailments. As far back as 3000 B.C., the Babylonians knew and used garlic as a curative aid. The physicians and priests in ancient Egypt fed garlic to the thousands of slaves that worked on the Cheops pyramid in order to keep up their strength. The Phoenicians and Vikings carried large amounts of garlic with them on their sea voyages.

Sometimes the garlic bulb is called a clove. It is so important that during the last World War, the British Government made a desperate call for the public to sell all the garlic they could provide. As a result thousands of tons were bought for the purpose of treating wounds of the troops returning from France and the front lines. It helped to prevent infection and healed wounds more rapidly. It is said that among the thousands of wounded men treated with garlic not one case of infection was found.

Others have stated that it helps in the treatment of tuberculosis, although I am not prepared to say that this is correct. But it is known to lower blood pressure, clear the skin of pimples, abscesses, boils, carbuncles and ulcers.

Herbs are special in the sense that the SUGMAD (God) made them for a purpose, and that purpose must have been for the healing of the embodiment of man and to separate Soul and body—to give Soul its opportunity to travel in the other worlds, provided it could do this in no other way.

One must heal himself before attending to

24

anything else. He must undertake a rigid period in which all foods are consumed which are known as the ECK (positive) foods. Too much emphasis is placed upon the *Kal* (negative) foods and they have become the bane of civilization.

Government reports link cancer and heart disease with cigarettes and tobacco smoking, but little or no mention is ever made of the *Kal* foods and drinks. These include coffee, tea, soft drinks, refined sugar, desserts, potatoes, tomatoes, to name a few.

Coffee and cigarettes are foremost on such a list of *Kal* substances. If one will stay on a rice diet of any sort, especially brown rice, for ten days or more, his health will improve. He can gradually go back to a balanced diet consisting of ECK and *Kal* foods. It is necessary to eliminate the impurities in the physical body first, then begin the balanced diet. It will give help to the physical system and put the mental faculties on greater alertness.

Generally, after the fifth day of any ECK diet plan, one finds himself in a difficult state of health. His head aches; he may have diarrhea or may be very nauseated. All these are bodily protests against the purification plan. It is *Kal's* own way of trying to keep the body from throwing off the toxic poisons. The pain and aches result from the fact that the body does not want to turn loose any of its problems.

Once we revert to a diet that consists of hardly anything other than herbs, we find illness becoming a doorway to health, tragedy turning to comedy and disaster heralding blessings.

Never eat a meal in a restaurant unless you are able to select from the a la carte menu, where you are more likely to find the type of herbs, fruits, and plants cooked closer to your natural diet.

For centuries eating and drinking among the ECK chelas has been steeped in the ceremony of a traditional sacramental rite.

With the ECK chela, the kitchen and dining room

have always been a sacred part of the home. Those rooms contain the basic but continuing mystery of life. Therein, the sacrifice of the plant and animal kingdom for the perpetuation of human life and thought is reenacted daily. All of ECK, as far as its worldly continuation goes, is based upon the establishment of health and happiness here and now. Of course, ECK deals with the hereafter, but it does not try to avoid what man has to do with his own responsibilities on earth today.

Without nourishment for the body, no life is possible. To eat in some form—whether it is like those particular ECK Masters of the ancient Order of the Vairagis, the God Eaters, who partake of the ECK life force, or the man on the material level with two full meals a day—is to create new life for tomorrow through the sacrifice of the lower realms, including the herbal kingdom. It was learned long ago that the body structure changes by eating, that the nature of man can be changed by the manner in which he eats and drinks. Therefore, eating and drinking are considered the most important ritual in the art of life, the creation of health and happiness.

Health and happiness means to be rid of fatigue and disease. To have a good appetite, good memory, good humor, and precision in thought and action. To be free from anxiety and fear. To have a great capacity for survival over illness and anxieties. To have joy, long life, and great spiritual adventures.

One does not need a great deal of sleep, but when he does, it should be sound, relaxed, and restful.

No man can have great spiritual experiences with a diseased body and mind. It has happened, I grant you, but it is rarely the case, for most of us need sound health in order to have some sort of opportunity to do Soul Traveling or out-of-the-body movement.

One's food intake must contain minerals in a balanced supply for the building and maintaining of health.

First, there is *Calcium*, which is essential for good bone structure, strong teeth, calm nerves, and good muscle tone. The body needs about one gram of calcium daily. The best natural sources of calcium are fresh fruits, vegetables, particularly green leafy vegetables, whole grains, milk, cheese, nuts, dark and blackstrap molasses, soybeans, soybean flour, and bone meal.

Second, we need *Chlorine*, which is a constituent of the acid in the gastric juice of the stomach. It aids in the purification and cleansing of the bodily system.

Chlorine stimulates the liver to act as a filter for waste products. It also stimulates production of hydrochloric acid, enzymatic digestive juice for fibrous foods.

A deficiency of chlorine could cause the loss of hair and teeth and improper digestive power. It is found in kelp, dulse, seagreens, leafy green vegetables, rye flour, and ripe olives.

Third, we have *Phosphorus*, which is equally good for the teeth and bone structure, as well as for brain tissue and the nervous system. Phosphorus is found in the structure of the nucleus of every body cell. It also assists in the maintenance of the acid-alkaline balance of the human body system. Both calcium and phosphorus are necessary in the diet for the former assists in the assimilation of phosphorus. Most of our foods do have phosphorus in large quantities, such as whole grains, dairy products, eggs, meat, beans, peas and nuts, and most fruits and vegetables.

Fourth, we find that *Iron* is essential for building the red blood cells. These red blood cells have the responsibility of bringing oxygen to the cells of the body and taking away carbon dioxide. A deficiency of iron creates a lack of red blood cells and this brings about anemia and low blood pressure. It is the magnetic element which attracts oxygen.

High blood pressure is caused by too much sodium

thickening the blood, and this requires more heart action to pump the blood. The "thin blooded" condition is caused by not having enough iron in the blood. When there is not sufficient iron balance in the body, either condition can occur.

Nearly all the foods which we eat have iron and oxygen. Wheat and most cereals contain iron in the form of iron phosphate, as do vegetables, such as beets, tomatoes, spinach, lettuce, cabbage, celery, carrots, turnips, squash, parsley, mustard greens, dandelion leaves, etc. But the principal source is in fruits.

It might appear that this information is not connected with herbs, but it must be pointed out that all vegetables are herbs, whether they are called foods or medicines. We also must remember that minerals are the products of herbs and therefore, must be considered in the study. It is also to be said that one ounce of prevention is worth a pound of cure, and whenever the chela will assimilate and keep the fundamentals of herbal studies in mind, he will be more successful in attaining results.

Fifth, is *Iodine*. A tiny amount of this mineral is needed in the body metabolism to maintain the metabolic balance in the physical system. This tiny bit of iodine is so important that it is better to take an over-supply than chance being under-supplied. The lack of iodine causes many deficiency symptoms such as goiter, unbalanced fat deposits, and even the appearance of stupidity. It is said that a tiny amount of this mineral can make the difference between a genius and an imbecile.

The thyroid gland located at the base of the throat regulates the body metabolism and requires small amounts of iodine daily to function properly. It is found in sea foods, animal and vegetable products, cod liver oil, dehydrated sea kelp, dulse, and raw sea salt.

The sixth mineral is *Copper*, necessary for the

proper utilization of iron in the body and the prevention of anemia. The best sources of copper are sea foods, liver, molasses, green leafy vegetables, soy products, egg yolk, whole grains and fruits, particularly dried fruits. Apricots are especially rich in copper and iron.

The seventh mineral is *Sodium*, which keeps the body in acid-alkaline balance and is necessary to keep calcium in solution for body needs. Salt, which is sodium chloride, is the principal source of sodium. However, it is found in vegetables and muscle meats. Celery is particularly rich in sodium. A lack of sodium could result in muscle cramps, heat strokes, stomach and intestinal gas, weight loss and muscle shrinkage. It favors the formation of saliva, gastric juice, enzymes, and other intestinal juices.

Sodium is also found in sea foods, poultry, beets, chard, and dandelion greens.

The eighth mineral is *Potassium*. It is important for body growth. Like sodium, it functions as a balancer, for sodium and potassium are needed in combination to help the body cells absorb nourishment from the bloodstream. It also assists in ridding the cells of waste matter. Dark and blackstrap molasses, dulse, kelp, leafy green vegetables, whole grains, fruits and almonds are good sources of potassium.

A deficiency of potassium will cause constipation, nervous disorders, insomnia, slow and irregular heart beat, and muscle damage. It sometimes causes the bones to become brittle and the kidneys to enlarge.

The ninth mineral is *Magnesium*, which is necessary to maintain mineral balance in the body in hot weather and to promote sleep. It is an aid in digestion and in the elimination of foods. The best source of magnesium is found in figs, lemons, grapefruit, corn, wild rice, almonds, oil rich nuts and seeds, apples, and celery.

About seventy per cent of the magnesium found in the body is in the bones. The rest is in the soft tissues

29

and blood. Muscle tissue contains more magnesium than calcium. It plays an important part as a co-enzyme in the building of protein.

A lack of magnesium will often cause irritability, unhappiness, and an interference with normal sleep.

The tenth mineral is *Manganese*. This mineral gives strength to the tissues and bones and protects the inner lining of the heart and blood vessels. It works closely with the B-complex vitamins to overcome laziness, sterility, and marital weakness. It also combines with phosphate, an enzyme to build strong bones. It is necessary to human growth and health.

Manganese is related to the use of calcium and phosphorus and is found in the bones. Green leaves and whole grains contain a great amount of manganese when they are grown on good soil. Manganese is a good activator of the enzymes in our bodies.

This mineral can also be found in green leaves, peas, beets, egg yolks, and unmilled grains.

The eleventh mineral is *Fluorine*, which helps build bones and tooth enamel and establishes the resistance of the body to disease and sickness. This is the natural fluorine which I am speaking about here, and it is found in many of the foods already named under the categories of the other minerals. It is said that when an excess is taken into the body, there is an adverse reaction upon internal organs, and there will be a weakening of the bone structure of the body.

The twelfth category of minerals includes *Carbon*, *Hydrogen*, *Oxygen* and *Nitrogen*. Of all the elements that go to make up the cells of the human body it is said that these minerals are by far the most abundant, as they are essential in all organic foods.

Few people ever realize the importance of these particular minerals because they seem so commonplace among the thirty known minerals which assist in the body structure of man.

The thirteenth mineral is *Sulphur*, known as nature's beauty mineral, for it keeps the hair glossy, the complexion smooth and youthful. It also invigorates the bloodstream and makes it resistant to bacterial infection. It works on the liver to secrete bile, maintains an overall body balance, and influences the health of the brain tissues. The foods which contain sulphur are fish, eggs, cabbage, lean beef, dried beans, Brussels sprouts, and many of the leafy vegetables.

The fourteenth mineral is *Silicon*, responsible for keeping the skin firm, the body filled with vitality, the eyes bright and cheerful. It is found in the hair, muscles, nails, cellular walls and connective tissues. It joins with other minerals to create tooth enamel and build strong bones. It is also said to be a builder of resistance to tuberculosis.

The food sources which are best for silicon are buckwheat products, mushrooms, carrots, tomatoes, liver, whole grains and lentils.

The fifteenth mineral is *Zinc*, a constituent of insulin, and male reproductivity. It is created in the pancreas where it helps store the glycogen, an energy producing substance for the body. It combines with phosphorus to aid in respiration and in sparking vitamin action. It helps in tissue respiration, the intake of oxygen, and the expulsion of carbon dioxide and toxic wastes. Insulin is dependent upon zinc for functioning. The lack of insulin in the body leads to diabetes. Zinc helps food become absorbed through the intestinal walls and is part of the stomach enzymes. It assists in the manufacture of male hormones and connects with carbohydrates and energy.

There are thirty known minerals, all of which influence our health and personality, but the fifteen given here are the essential ones which are needed for maintaining the body at a top efficiency level. Each of them needs the other minerals, for together, they assist vitamins, proteins, amino acids, enzymes, carbohydrates, fats, sugars, and other necessary elements in the body.

Since most foods are deficient in essential minerals and vitamins due to poor soil and unfavorable marketing conditions, it is almost necessary to supplement the diet with bottled natural minerals and vitamins. There are a good many brands of natural minerals and vitamins on the market which can be recommended by physicians and health authorities.

The survey of the means by which the separation of Soul from the bondage of the body is accomplished would be far from complete if we did not take up the Homeric and Eleusinian mysteries. Nectar, the drink of the Olympian gods, was an infallible means of initiation into the mysteries of the beyond by the automatic release of Soul from bodily bondage.

Next we find the initiated Brahmans, the priests of the Hindu religion, using what is known as the soma drink. This was similar to the Greek nectar quaffed by the gods of Olympia. The cup of Kykeon, which was drunk at the Eleusinian mysteries initiation, was similar to both the Hindu and Greek god drinks.

He who would drink it easily reached the Brahma, the plane of splendor. The soma drink known to the Europeans was not the same as the one the Asiatics knew. Only the initiated can taste the real soma, and even the kings and rajas, when performing the sacrificial rites, received the substitute.

It is true that the priests of the present day orders have lost the secret of the true soma drink. It cannot be found in the rituals or the secret books anymore, nor through oral information. The true followers of the Vedic religion are now deceased, and the soma drink commemorated in the Hindu Pantheon, which was called the King-soma, is gone, too. Whoever drank the King-soma participated in the heavenly kingdom. He became filled with the holy ECK and was purified of his sins.

The soma made a new man of the initiate; he was reborn and transformed, and his spiritual nature overcame the physical. It bestowed the divine power of inspiration and developed the clairvoyant faculty to the utmost. According to the esoteric explanation, the soma was a plant, but at the same time, it was an angel. It forcibly connected the inner, the highest of man, which is Soul, with the Atma-Sarup (Soul body), and thus united by the power of the magic drink, soared above the physical nature and participated during life in the beatitude and ineffable glories of heaven.

The soma drink was a true plant which the priests used in the ancient rituals to separate Soul from the body during initiations in the mystery cults. We believe this to be Frankincense, which was used in the ancient days for religious rituals, and if used as an incense, it was believed to bring the mind to devotion, producing a detached state of separation of Soul and body. It is said that the herb, which is a gum resin from various trees, was heated until it became a liquid, then mixed with honey and goat's milk. This became a powerful ingredient which would give the initiate the first step on the path of separation of Soul from the body.

The ECK Masters never used this sort of assistance for their chelas, because they felt that it was better to learn how to separate Soul and body with a clear consciousness. (The true disciple of ECKANKAR is likely to be misunderstood by other men; they do not perceive that he is ever pursuing death and dying. Nature has designed man to leave his physical body at will, transcend to higher planes, then return to the body. The Living ECK Master helps each aspirant personally, and each chela receives practical experience, however little. It may be during the very first sitting during his initial experience with the spiritual exercises of ECK, or later. A person who is competent to give man this personal experience of withdrawal or separation from the body temporarily, and who can put him on the way to the higher spiritual realms is the Living ECK Master, the Mahanta, the *Vi-Guru*.)

The enzymes are delicate life-like substances found in all living cells, whether vegetable or animal. Their presence and strength can be determined only by means of refined tests. Enzymes break up into small molecules—proteins, fats, starches, maltose, sucrose, lactose and cellulose.

The function of the enzyme is to aid in the digestion of food. It is any of a class of complex organic substances such as amylose, pepsin, etc., that accelerate specific chemical transformations, as in the digestion of foods, in plants and animals.

They are specialized protein catalysts which regulate the speed of the many chemical reactions involved in the metabolism of living organisms. The word is derived from the Greek phrase enzyme, meaning "in leaven."

Enzymes are classified into several broad categories, such as hydrolytic, oxidizing, and reducing, depending upon the type of reaction which they control. Nature puts enzymes into all foods together with vitamins, minerals, fats, proteins, carbohydrates, and water. However, all this food is completely indigestible until enzymes work on it and break down complex foods into simpler substances, which the bloodstream can then absorb.

There is an enzyme to help build phosphorus into bone and nerve tissues in the body. Another enzyme helps fix iron in the red blood cells. Enzymes can change protein into fat or sugar. Enzymes change carbohydrates into fat and enzymes change fats into carbohydrates.

Some enzymes, such as pepsin and trypsin, which bring about the digestion of meat, control a great many different reactions, while others such as urease, which controls urea decomposition, are extremely specific and may accelerate only one reaction.

Enzymes perform in a few minutes chemical transformations which are impossible to perform in laboratories. Without the help of enzymes we could stuff ourselves with herbs and foods but literally starve to death. The length of the life of enzymes depends upon temperature. When enzymes are subjected to boiling temperatures for even a few minutes they are completely destroyed. Boiling potatoes, meats or leafy vegetables in water often cause complete destruction of the enzymes contained therein.

Enzymes in the dormant state are found usually as dry seeds, and are able to retain their activity for hundreds of years. They have been found in the Egyptian mummies, which are over three thousand years old, in rice several hundred years in age, and in the flesh of ancient mammoths found frozen in the Arctic regions. These are said to be over fifty thousand years old and to be in a well-preserved condition. Enzymes can be preserved indefinitely when dried to a powder at blood heat and by extreme cold.

Enzymes as a class are extraordinarily efficient. An ounce of pepsin, for example, can digest nearly two tons of egg white in a few hours.

Sun ripened fruits and vegetables are rich in enzymes. The sun causes enzymes to function as they need warmth and moisture. But there is a difference between the sun warmth and the boiling process over a fire during cooking. Therefore, in the manufacturing and cooking of foods, many enzymes are lost and the food value is lowered. The work is thrown upon the glands, organs, muscles and fluids of the body.

As each of us grows older, the quota of enzymes in the body gradually diminishes, and eventually, we die. This means that we are as old as our enzymes. This is why the longevity of the ECK Masters is an established fact. They have learned to control the enzymes in their physical bodies. But the normal person can keep his body functioning well under general conditions, as long as he has sufficient enzymes in his stomach to digest the foods that he eats.

In order to have less wear on the body and to save it from aging too fast, one can try to take into his body the exogenous enzymes—those enzymes which are derived from raw foods. It is these uncooked, unprocessed foods which give the body the exogenous enzymes. The more enzymes consumed in the raw and uncooked foods, the fewer the body will have to manufacture on its own.

Knowledge about enzymes proves the relationship between good health and long life of the ECK Masters. Their diet, which consists largely of natural uncooked foods, includes fruits and vegetables, mostly in an unaltered state from the soil to their mouths.

One of the best enzymes that a person can find for his health is contained in pineapple. This is the reason the peoples of the South Seas Islands remained in such general good health before the coming of the white man. The papaya also ranks high in enzymes. Either one or the other should be eaten with every meal if possible, as both are high in enzymes which greatly aid the digestion.

Some of the other foods which may be added to our diet to help with the intake of minerals, proteins, vitamins, enzymes, and other essential ingredients for good health are: almonds, coconuts, pecans, walnuts, hazelnuts, lecithin, honey, wheat germ, brewer's yeast, yogurt, buttermilk, fish, kidneys, liver, apricots, pumpkins, sesame, apples, eggs, cottage cheese and sun-ripened dried fruits. These are not all, of course, only a few to get you started on the right path to better health and longevity.

## Chapter Three

## THE HERBS THAT GIVE LIFE
## FOR THE VITAL POWERS

Half of the population of the United States suffers from some form of chronic disease and only a small percentage of all Americans are free from any kind of physical ailment or defect, according to the report of the U.S. Special Commission on the Nation's Health given to the President in December, 1964.

We have more mental hospitals and sanitoriums, more psychiatrists and psychoanalysts than any country in the world, but it has been estimated that one out of every ten Americans may spend some part of his life in a mental institution.

Where did man drop off the path to the natural means of health from herbs, plants, minerals, and vitamins and begin on the path of chemistry for his health? Somewhere back in the Middle Ages and the beginning of this modern age, Lavoisier, Pasteur, Harvey, Cesalpino, Schleiden, and others might have taken the wrong turn on the path to good health and led humanity downhill to the bottom of the ladder. Nature is the destroyer of all living organisms and there is not much man can do about it, despite all his wonderful advances in a science that is praised as being the greatest in all history. Soul is immortal, but man as the body will be born, live and die like everything else in the world.

Sir Thomas Browne, a physician, who lived in merry old England, made the statement, "Death is the only cure to every problem of man, but everybody that I know seems to be fighting off the cure." In time all must die. It is only the ECK Masters who have the secrets for longevity, and it is hardly thinkable that they are going to give out their knowledge to the masses of the world.

The world is already overpopulated and nature always has a way of taking care of this phenomenon whenever it takes place on earth. If a major war does not depopulate the human race so others might live, then a vast catastrophe takes place and a large part of the masses of people are taken out of their bodies. This is why the Living ECK Master is now striving so hard to arouse Souls to get out of their bodies and return to the higher worlds so they will not have to be reincarnated into this world where a major cataclysm is going to take place.

However, we find in the human system a need for living in better health in the present moment. There is a remedy through herbs, plants, diet, fasting, and the philosophy of ECKANKAR. You may call it the ECK diet, for through it you can find your way to health once more.

One must begin an independent study at the very roots of his nutritional necessities. He must seek to learn the physical, chemical, and biological origin of his body. He should put aside all psychological and spiritual questions until later. He begins with the theory and practice of nutrition, of which the first principles are: (1) Everything in the organic world exists through the intake of air, water, food, and rest by sleep. (2) Anything that has life and does not have an intake of air, water, food, and rest by sleep will soon die.

The primary note of man here is that food is to be eaten in order for the survival of the body. Survival is also the concern of the most spiritual of mankind, for even those spiritual giants who have walked the earth ate food, breathed air, and drank water. The body is a transformation of food; therefore, eating is being.

In Atlantis, flowers, cereals—both wild and

cultivated—grew in great abundance and variety, including one fruit which is known to have had a hard rind and to have provided meat and ointment. This was the coconut, for Atlantis was in a semi-tropical zone and many of the crops raised were from the southern climate flora and plants. The Atlanteans had orchards and reapable crops. Most of their cereal crops were wheat, oats, barley, rye, and maize. Their meats were produced from domesticated animals, especially raised for the purpose of feeding the massive population of Atlantis.

During my incarnations in Atlantis, which are now ancient memories, the people were tall, fair-haired, with good figures and blue eyes. Those inhabitants of Lemuria, in the area of what is now the Pacific Ocean, as I remember, were fairly tall, slender, with dark olive skins and brown or black eyes and hair.

The people of both continents were great fish eaters, more than beef or pork. This was due to the fact that they did not care for the slaughter of animals, but were more inclined to eat fish and fowl with plants, vegetables, and herbs. They were eaters of cereals, especially wheat, in great abundance for it increased their virility and made them strong and manly.

They ate a great deal of fresh fruit, flat wheat wafers, buck loin, fish, chicken or birds of any nature which the professional hunters would trap by the scores and sell to the open air markets in the large public squares of the many vast cities on Atlantis. Most of their meats, however, were roasted. They never ate fried meat because it was considered to be bad for the stomach.

The tradition and policy of the Atlanteans about meat was that it was well to eat it, but not as a staple diet. Animal flesh contained, so they believed, certain properties which were of value when taken with discretion. But eaten frequently, and in too large a quantity, meat would coarsen the body and lead to many of the internal complaints which are so prevalent among the races of the world today.

A liquid drink was made from the coconut milk which was an opaque, green-yellow color. It was a fruit juice diluted with coconut milk and water, mixed with limes and grendallias.

They also had a cordial to aid the digestion. It was a dark, sticky, green liquor, not unlike Chartreuse. It was flavored with flowers and herbs and was highly alcoholic. The taste was fiery and would cause a warm glow in the stomach and body when swallowed.

The peoples of Atlantis bathed in hot springs with an oil that would act as a lather. These springs were housed in stone buildings similar to the Roman baths. Mixed bathing was quite popular and few considered this more than a social gathering of families who would visit, while at the same time they washed, rested, bathed, and sunned themselves. Most of them wore light clothes similar to Roman togas and gowns because the weather was mild.

Whenever they wished to eat, especially the peasant class, they would gather fresh fruit which was in season and net a fish in the lake or river and cook it. All waste products were disposed of by burying in the soil. They tapped the sunlight for many things—for example, heating water in containers which would be under a sort of glass similar to our violet ray.

The Atlanteans had thirty thousand years in which to develop their civilization and little wonder that it was greater than anything we find on earth today. They were able to control all the world by force of arms and political means, as most of it was colonized by the Atlanteans. When modern man is able to fully explore the other planets there will be found ruins of a civilization which cannot be explained. It will be the remains of colonies which the Atlanteans settled upon these planets for trade purposes, and because they were becoming overcrowded in their homeland.

These colonies died away when Atlantis sunk beneath the waves centuries ago.

Besides the raising of cereals in abundance on Atlantis, there were low root crops—radishes, carrots, turnips, lettuce, dwarf beans, peas, potatoes, broccoli, cabbage, artichokes. There were also many others whose names would not be at all familiar to the reader, such as the atoge, which was a type of yellow corn, and the vladige, a type of sweet potato.

Many of their herbal formulas consisted of tonics, aromatics, laxatives, purgatives, and antispasmodics. Herbs, seeds, roots, and plants accomplished much for the general health of the Atlantis nation. Among those which were used most in the general curative formulas were celery, muskroot, vervain, jasmine, coriander, cyclamen, navelwort, wild poppy, periwinkle, purslane, maiden hair, valerian, anemone, endive, myrtle, mandrake, cloves, cinnamon, cardamon, and hemlock.

The Living ECK Master (known as Supaku) of one of the high periods of the civilization of Atlantis helped to compile a number of the herbs, roots, seeds, flowers, and plants which were researched in the government health laboratories. Some of these were:

Angelica, a domestic herb used to give added strength when the body needed an extra push. The Atlanteans used this for their common foot soldiers in battle; also, as a stomach medicine for gas and as a mild diuretic.

Aniseed or anise was another plant used by the Atlanteans. The oil was used as a base for liquors, and, as today, in preparations for pectoral troubles arising from colds, coughs, etc. Anise was also used as a medicine for the relief of intestinal gases caused by meals consisting of too much pork and beef.

Basil, another herb of the mint family, was used a great deal by the Atlanteans. It is a sweet herb characterized by a pleasant, aromatic smell and taste.

It was used for seasoning and flavoring foods, and for intestinal gases and mild nervous disorders. It is still being used for the same purpose in modern times.

Camomile, a plant of the aster family, was often used by the Atlanteans. It has strong scented foliage and flower heads which contain a bitter medicinal principle. It is used as an antispasmodic, stomachic, and as a perspiration producing ingredient for breaking fevers. It was then used for nervous conditions of the body, poultices for allaying pain, and when made as a tea, was effective as a sedative. It also made a good hair shampoo lotion.

Comfrey is an herb, a very useful one, which is known today. In those ancient times it was described by a word which we would call "knitbone." It was used mainly as a poultice for diseased and fractured bones. It was also utilized in tubercular and chest diseases; a mixture of goat's milk, about a pint of boiled water, with an ounce or two of crushed comfrey root or leaves. The root was treated as a vegetable by boiling, and it was very delicious with the juice of a lime or a lemon.

The common Dandelion was another plant which the Atlanteans made use of for kidney and liver disorders. They also used its root for roasting and making what we call coffee today.

The Garlic bulb was the miracle herb of its day in those ancient times, as it is in this modern era. It was used as a sweat-producing herb to break fevers, as a diuretic, and as a healing agent for wounds both inner and outer. It was made into a syrup with honey and used by those who had common colds and respiratory diseases, just as it is today.

The Atlanteans used Ground Ivy as an astringent, diuretic, and tonic for kidney diseases and indigestion. Also, Horehound was a popular form of the herbal pectoral remedies. There was Hyssop, which they used for healing wounds, coughs, and lung complaints; and the Marjoram Sweet and the

Marjoram Pot and Mint for nausea, sickness, and children's illnesses. They used Nettles, Parsley, Rosemary, Rue, Tansy, Thyme, Wormwood, Cyclamen, Mugwort, Valerian, Satyrion as well as a dozen others which are unknown today.

I have used the modern terms for these herbs, because the Atlanteans had different names for each which probably could not be pronounced because of the difference in the languages of that day and the present form of English. But we do know that apricots were the staple food of the Atlanteans. They used them in everything, and they carried them as a dried food for long voyages by ships that sailed the seas and by interplanetary airships.

We know that all foods have a vegetal origin. Animals could not exist without the vegetal. The human body cannot digest inorganic substances. It cannot manufacture carbohydrates, fats, or minerals from inorganic substances. The synthesis of inorganic substances is a vegetal function, a process called autotropism. This is a phenomenon performed by the vegetable kingdom in which it absorbs inorganic elements and converts them into organic foods—a miracle of composition and creation produced by the interworking forces of nature which no laboratory has yet been able to duplicate.

Whether it is worth man's efforts to be a meat eater is still a moot question. A few persons have demonstrated the value of giving up meat if one is going to have spiritual unfoldment, and others have demonstrated that meat eating has little influence on whether a person gets spiritual unfoldment or not.

However, we first take up the vegetable kingdom as an individual part of the eating process for health factors in man. The vegetable kingdom works ceaselessly to produce the leaves, grains, tubers, and fruits which feed fleshly organisms, such as animals and man. The vegetable is mother to the animal and human species. These leaves, grains, tubers, and fruits are transformed into animal tissue by the process of digestion and assimilation.

Man is the child of the vegetal mother, so say some people who are close students of herbs, plants, and flowers. Without vegetable life, so they claim, no animal or human life could survive on earth. This is accepted, of course, for we are utterly dependent directly or indirectly upon vegetable and fruit produce for our physical survival. The hemoglobin of the blood cells is derived from chlorophyl. All vegetal foods are the virgin materials for the maintenance and construction of body tissues, so this means we must have vegetables as our basic food and this is a biological and fundamental law.

Many people are vegetarians for this reason, yet the law does not apply to all people, as stated before, for there are many who simply cannot be vegetarians because of something in their physical systems which will not allow it.

Too many of those who believe that the chemistry of men is uniform learn in the long run that what one thinks is right about dieting can be all wrong. No two people can follow the same diet for many reasons. One may be karmic conditions, another could be the environmental conditions learned at mother's knee. Physical heredity and astrological influences may also contribute to individual differences.

No two people have the same reaction to a given food intake. Where as one person can be a good vegetarian, another would become ill if put on such a diet for any length of time. Some ECK Masters, the adepts of the ancient Order of Vairagi, have been meat eaters, not heavy, of course, but they were eaters of fish and fowl. Others within the order have been pure vegetarians. They are above the body consciousness and cannot be affected by what is put in their bodies in the way of food. Naturally, none of them drink or smoke.

The idea of vegetarianism is an old one. Traditionally, it has been linked with the spiritual growth of man via the Oriental religions. Millions in India, China, Japan, and other countries of the Far East have for centuries followed the vegetarian diet. Vegetarianism started in the ancient days when the domestic animal was a scarce item and the *Law of Manu*, which possibly appeared as the law book which codified the ancient Hindu law, said that the killing of the cow was a religious taboo.

This law book also included mythology, cosmogony, metaphysical doctrines, techniques of government, duties of the various castes, and the doctrines of immortality and transmigration of Soul.

There was a judge in India during these ancient times who tried to help the poor by decreeing the killing of a cow as a violation of civil law in order to protect the family's supply of dairy products. Families in those early days had to depend upon the cow's milk, butter, and cheese as their main source of food. If a neighbor, or a thief, stole the cow and butchered it for meat, the family was left destitute.

The law did not work very well, so the civil authorities decided that it would be better to incorporate it into the *Law of Manu* as sacred law to be enforced by the priestcraft. To this day the cow is sacred in India, and much of the population will not eat meat because of this. Hence vegetarianism became a necessity with millions of the poor in India as a sort of religious tradition. It has become a fixed idea in the minds of many of the religious teachers, who claim that only the vegetarians shall have spiritual enlightenment.

Other countries such as China, Japan, and the nations of southeast Asia also have their traditions of vegetarianism, but this has been more out of necessity, because of the lack of domestic animals for human consumption.

During primitive times there was not enough food

to supply the teeming population, so a majority of people in the Asian countries became vegetarians. However, we find today that the people on a whole are not healthy in these countries. They are small in stature and are generally in bad health with short life spans.

In the beginning we find that the ECK (positive or God) foods and the *Kal* (negative) foods are just opposite in nature. The *Kal* is always opposite to, and antagonistic to, the ECK, yet it cannot exist without its superior which is the ECK. In this relativistic material world, the ECK is antithetical and opposite to the *Kal.* Happiness is the opposite to sadness, and beauty is the opposite of ugliness. Each thing within this universe is supported, animated, maintained and is in opposition to, its opposite. This is the great law of the SUGMAD, which is the order of the universe. It is the very simple yet profound law which rules our life in this relative world as distinguished from the true world of spirit, that which is absolute, infinite and eternal.

If one has violated the great law of the universe, he could die prematurely because of illness or accident. The ECK is tolerant and forgiving to the very end. But if we violate its laws, while living in this world of matter, energy, space and time, we must pay the penalty. There is no excuse for being ignorant of the law. If we are ill it is only meant to be a warning, an alarm signal and not a punishment. Too many ignore the divine alarm signal and go to the drugstore to find a pain relieving drug on the shelf. The use of drugs or drastic means to heal by patent medicines and other methods only serves to destroy the delicate telephonic alarm signals.

There are two things that are harmful to the body—one is that drugs will only arrest the progress of a disease, but seldom cure it; second, the drugs generally are devoid of morality and spirituality, having been developed at any cost and method to destroy the symptoms of disease. Drugs often create more serious illness and disease in future generations by arresting a malady at its present stage of progress within the body.

The essential aim of ECK is to lead man to infinite freedom, absolute justice, and eternal happiness by the means of Soul Travel. We keep running into problems with the aim of ECKANKAR, because most people want to make a garbage pail of their bodies and regard spirituality as something separate from their health.

This is not true, for health has a bearing upon the spiritual development of each individual, whether he knows it or not. That is, the state of the body has an influence upon the mind, and the mind, in turn, can affect the spiritual side of those not yet trained in the spiritual arts of Soul Travel. When one has reached a certain stage of spiritual unfoldment, he will have self-discipline so that nothing can affect him. This is known as the *Vairag*, or the true detachment from the material world. But at the stage of spiritual unfoldment that most people have reached at the present time, few have any discipline whatsoever.

Behavior rising from diseased or sick bodies has direct influence upon the non-disciplined person and will affect his mental attitude as well as his food intake. Therefore, the man seeking spiritual enlightenment will become acquainted with herbs, minerals, plants, and flowers as a means of improving his health. Then he can concentrate on his spiritual unfoldment, instead of a body which reflects illness and pain.

The knowledge of nutrition that we find in the ECK knowledge of herbs offers much toward the curing of some basic illnesses in the individual. There are several levels of medicaments which should be of interest. First, the symptomatic remedy, which is a palliative means of removing symptoms. Second, the preventive remedy, which arrests an illness or keeps it

47

from happening. Third, the study of the means of attaining better physical, mental, and spiritual health. Fourth, the *Kal* (negative) means of trying to keep the body healthy by narcotics or similar drugs. Fifth, the social and educational means, which establishes health institutions for the public at large. Sixth, the remedy of mental and philosophical means, directed to the plane of thought and self-help (i.e. certain forms of yoga and other spirito-materialistic philosophies which have to do with exercises of the mind and body). Last, is the ECK (God or positive) method of finding health. Through Soul Travel, which lifts one above this physical plane of consciousness, one can see and repair whatever damage is done to the body and brain.

Those in ECKANKAR know that there are several methods of taking care of the physical health of the body and mind: by the intake of herbs, minerals, vitamins, fruits, plants, and flowers in the correct form; by prayer, which is seldom used by any ECK chela; by contemplation or the use of the spiritual exercises of ECK; and last, by Soul Travel itself. If one is praying, using meditation, or any of the esoteric methods of asking God for healing, he may be answered in different ways. First, his prayer might be answered on the physical level by someone indirectly suggesting that he use certain medications, herbs, remedies, or that he see a particular physician. The second way in which he might receive help is through the inner senses flashing a message for guidance in a certain direction. The third method is, of course, direct healing from the Living ECK Master or from other divine sources which render the healing possible.

To find the particular remedy that will eliminate the cause of an ailment for good is the purpose of the ECK methods. The ECK remedy is the highest way, and, indeed, simplest in its method, but deepest in its philosophical foundation. Since the ultimate cause of every illness is a violation of the order of the universe through ignorance, few attack this cause and restore their health. The ECK way of restoring health is through patience, using philosophy and education in the spiritual works of ECK in order to get the chela to know something about himself.

The ECK way is to show man how to release his own innate abilities so that he might achieve successful attempts at good judgment, good health within this world, success at Soul Travel, and spiritual perfection leading to God-Realization.

It is true that faith has a great deal to do with the healing of the body and mind, but it is not everything. If faith could cure, then all those who make pilgrimages to Lourdes would be healed. Naturally, faith will heal some but, in a way, it might injure others who lack the understanding necessary for healing. Blind faith is often primitive, filled with superstitions, unguided, and misdirected.

It is said in the works of ECK that faith—that is, true faith—must insist upon the understanding of the divine cause of whatever life might be. This is, of course, an understanding of the laws of Karma, retribution and reincarnation. Thus, faith can be considered as knowledge, for without knowledge beyond the physical senses, there can be no true faith.

We find that most of us put blind faith in medicines. We hope that the health authorities will have enough knowledge to heal us or get rid of the cause of our illness. The use of medicine of itself requires blind faith. Who is man going to trust to help him get rid of all those causes of illness?

Those who follow the path of ECKANKAR, the Ancient Science of Soul Travel, know that it is best to put one's faith in the living ECK Master, who is really the MAHANTA, the living Divine Consciousness on earth, said to be symbolic of the ancient law that has prevailed over all life here in this

49

world. This is known to all ECK chelas as the Tejas, the radiant principle, that law of God which is the practical philosophy of the ECK and the *Kal.* The ECK power may be called the centripetal wave which is always moving toward the center (that is, the Heavenly Kingdom) the Ocean of Love and Mercy. The *Kal* power is that wave which is said to be moving away from the center of life.

The ECK and *Kal* are at the same time in opposition and yet complimentary to one another like day and night, summer and winter, man and woman. They are the fundamental opposites which destroy and unite to create everything that exists in the lower worlds.

Because in this world the ECK is always limited and relative, it means that the *Kal,* which is the lower world power, is also limited and relative. But here in this world they blend into each other like night and day. We find that nothing exists that is totally *Kal* or totally ECK in this world. It is either more *Kal* than ECK, or more ECK than *Kal,* so we must think of them as being one or the other.

This is the dualism which we read so much about in the sacred scriptures of the world. In this world of relativity we find that the ECK inevitably changes into the *Kal* and the *Kal* into the ECK. It is when we enter into the worlds of pure spirit above the *Atma,* the fifth, or Soul plane, that we find the absolute, eternal, and infinite.

We find that within this category of the ECK and *Kal* there are degrees of characteristics. The three fundamental characteristics are shape, weight, and color. We find that the ECK is not limited because it is the positive God force. Therefore, it will lack a shape, for it is a great wave which is collecting all Souls in the worlds of God and returning them to the great Ocean of Love and Mercy, from the negative pole to the highest of the worlds. It is like an ocean wave which feeds all life. It dominates all life in a weightless degree and in the pale colors which are pinks, oranges, high-yellows, light-greens, and sky-blues.

Everything in the universe can be classified as either ECK or *Kal* without getting into any complications. Most products grown in the cooler climates are ECK, in comparison with those grown in the warm climates. The red fruits from the northern climates (for example, apples) are ECK foods; while those like the purple mango from the tropical countries are listed among the *Kal* foods.

Therefore, we find that the *Kal* is the heavier of the two forces for it dwells in the lower worlds. It makes the solidness which we call the soil and other forms of inorganic life. Many of the colors of fruits, plants, and other organic foods are purple, dull-orange, indigo, dark-red, dark-green, black, and heavy-yellow.

We note that those who live in a temperate climate where the cooler weather is more prevalent are usually psychologically stronger than those races living in the tropics, because the former eat more ECK foods than the latter. Now we also find that the ECK foods are mildly sweet and pleasant tasting while the *Kal* foods are generally hot, pungent, sour, heavily sweet, bitter, and salty. This pertains only to the natural tastes and not to artificial flavors or those chemically treated. For example, chemically treated sugar is extremely *Kal* food, while raw and pure sugar is ECK food.

Most ECK foods are red or yellow, generally pale in color. We even find this true of meats which are to be found on the butcher's counter (not frozen or canned meats). This also is true of fish, eggs, and dairy products. We find the following are ECK foods: pumpkins, carrots, yams, apples, cherries, strawberries, brown rice, oranges, all vegetables, cereals, fruits and plants of natural pale colors. These are strong in vitamins, minerals, and enzymes.

The *Kal* foods are generally the artificially prepared foods. They are the pastries, pies, and breads made from refined flours and hydrogenated fats, chocolate flavoring, candy (unless it is made with pure sugar), soft drinks, synthetic ice cream. Also foods with a natural dark coloring, like eggplant, mango, pimento, red peppers or any other type of hot seasoning, watercress and dark red vegetables such as beans.

One should add lots of seeds to his diet which are ECK in nature, such as pumpkin, sesame, almond, and other types of nuts (not salted nuts, but those that have been roasted only in pure oil). One should also add to the diet Brewer's yeast, lecithin, and wheat germ. These products can be eaten with cottage cheese and salads or mixed in fruit juices and yogurt if one desires. Buttermilk can be included in the diet; and one should eat plenty of meat, especially brains, kidney, and liver. These are generally good for the human system.

The essential factor in this nutrition discussion about the ECK and *Kal* food value is that there should be a proper proportion of each for the human body to have the right nourishment daily. Unless this is done, one will suffer from a lack of, for example, potassium, a *Kal* product necessary for the nourishment and feeding of the body system. Potassium must be properly balanced in the body with sodium, an ECK product, in order to feed the body properly.

However, we find that the best all around food product, which contains a perfect balance between the ECK and the *Kal* foods, is natural, unpolished brown rice. If one's environmental habits are broken or disturbed and meat cannot be eaten because of some body ailment, he can turn to natural, unpolished brown rice to give him most of the nourishment his body needs for good health.

# Chapter Four

## THE MAGIC
## OF THE WONDER HERBS

Anyone who raises questions about man's health and philosophical nature must be prepared to answer those who come swarming to him about their own issues of life, be it here in the physical body or the spiritual self.

Evidence of man's desire for better health comes when he begins to pinpoint those few herbs and minerals which can give him special help. The wonder herbs are not many, although we can say that every plant and herb is a gift of God to man. Therefore, we can really look at each as a wonder herb.

It may clarify matters if it is pointed out that all vegetables are herbs, regardless of whether they are called foods or medicines. Unless there is a basic understanding of this fact, it is quite useless to study herbs. The chela who will assimilate and keep the fundamentals of herbology in mind will be more successful in attaining results.

A few herbs have been designated as miracle herbs—for example, the Comfrey, Licorice, Kelp, Alfalfa, Golden Seal, Parsley, and Motherwort. There are more, but these are the ones which are to be taken up in this chapter and discussed at length.

Nature's process of healing is gradual and always seems terribly slow to those who are suffering or impatient. While herbs will assist, it is always God who does the healing. To give up the harmful indulgences requires self-discipline on the part of the sufferer. But it must be done. Habits that have injured the body in the past must be dropped. We find those who persevere in self-discipline to abide by the laws of Spirit will gain results in body and mental health. No man living here in this material universe can go on disobeying the laws of this world and expect to have good health.

We shall first examine the wonder herb known as *comfrey*. It is native to Europe, but has been naturalized in America. It grows in moist places on low ground and it flowers all summer. The comfrey root is spindle-shaped and contains a large amount of mucilage which is best extracted with water. The root penetrates deeply into the soil.

Since ancient times the comfrey root has been used as a healing herb. It takes care of any part of the body that is torn or broken, externally or internally. It is a great aid for the healing of cells or in the production of new cells. It helps grow flesh and bone, stops hemorrhages, and is wonderful for coughs, soothing and healing the inflamed tissues in a most remarkable way.

The comfrey is a flowering plant that grows a few feet tall with slender leaves which are large and hairy, often lying low on the ground. They are so prickly that they can cause the skin to itch. The flowers are a dull white, and after blossoming, leave small black seeds. The root is long, spreads in thick branches underground, and is full of a glutinous, tasteless juice which is medicinal.

Comfrey had its origin, as far as can be traced, in the Caucasus Mountains in southern Russia. The plant contains a specific healing agent known as Allantoin, which is present in both roots and leaves. This substance has the ability of a cell-proliferant, making the edges of wounds grow together and healing sores. Taken as a tea, comfrey helps to overcome gastric or duodenal ulcers, or any irritation affecting the small or large intestines.

The comfrey plant has other valuable attributes

besides its healing properties. It can also be used as a delicious green salad leaf. The nutritional value is comparable to that of alfalfa. Comfrey contains nearly as much protein as alfalfa, about fifty percent higher mineral content, and is very rich in Carotene, the basis of Vitamin A. It makes a very good vegetable, for it can be prepared like spinach and has a similar taste.

Comfrey is used for many ailments such as asthma, tuberculosis, gastric disturbances, internal ulcerations, ulcers, rheumatic complaints, eczema, boils, and other skin troubles. Many persons say they eat better, sleep better, and feel much more fit after following a course of drinking comfrey tea or after ingesting comfrey in some other form prescribed by a physician or health authority.

Another point to make in behalf of the comfrey plant is that it is often given for ailments and for building strong bones in young animals. Many a good horse trainer who works with racing thoroughbreds will include comfrey leaves in the feeding of his horses.

Comfrey was used with such good results as a food in Russia during World War II that it has now become a staple part of the diet of the rural people. It is also grown experimentally as a fodder crop in several agricultural research centers in Australia. Many health authorities are beginning to recognize that the comfrey plant plays an important part in the medicinal treatment of many types of ailments and sicknesses.

It is reported that the people of Switzerland have used the comfrey root for centuries as an aid in relieving arthritis. Comfrey tea is supposedly a blood purifier, and has been used as such in European countries for years. Often the Europeans cook the leaves and eat them as we do spinach, chard, or beet greens.

*Kelp*, another wonder plant, is a common seaweed

which contains every vital mineral needed for sustaining bodily health. Among these minerals are: aluminum, barium, bismuth, boron, calcium, chlorine, chromium, cobalt, copper, gallium, iodine, magnesium, manganese, molybdenum, phosphorus, potassium, silicon, silver, sodium, strontium, sulphur, tin, titanium, vandium, and zirconium. Kelp takes all the vital mineral elements from the ocean water and converts them from inorganic substances into organic minerals, which can be used by man for health.

Harvested from the deep sea water where a treasure of minerals exist, Kelp is one of the best sources of iodine, iron, potassium, and chlorine. It has a good supply of phosphorus, too. All of these minerals join to build greater brain power.

We know that sea water is a veritable treasure trove of precious minerals, so whatever grows in the sea will absorb the same vital brain foods. Therefore, in order to have good health, one should use powdered kelp, as a flavoring agent for soups, salads, meats, baked dishes, and other dishes. Kelp tablets taken regularly will supply the iron, phosphorus, and potassium needed by the brain and other parts of the body.

Three special brain foods are lecithin, kelp, and desiccated liver. You must have these in your diet for top-level mental powers to help you through the day. Of the three, kelp is the best if you cannot get any of the others.

It is of interest to note that maritime nations, including the Japanese, Chinese, South Sea Islanders, and the Eskimos have for centuries prized seaweed among their principal vegetables. These people have been wise enough to have kelp in its varied forms as a staple in their diet. In continental Europe it is found that those living near the seashore have learned the value of seaweed, especially as a fodder for their cattle. This is particularly true in Denmark, where a dairy herd is given a supplementary feeding of dried seaweed to help increase milk production, as well as to produce a richer form of milk.

Kelp has for many years demonstrated its value as a remedy for human ailments resulting from deficiency conditions. It has been successful in relieving glandular disturbances which often result in goiter, rickets, anemia, underweight, constipation, stomach trouble, headache, kidney disorders, eczema, neuritis, asthma, and low vitality.

Malnutrition does not come from lack of food, but from the lack of proper nutrition. Deficiency disease has reached an all time high. In spite of the boastful claims of the authorities, we find among our own people, many of whom can purchase anything they desire to suit the palate, those who are lacking in proper foods.

Soil deficient in minerals cannot provide us with healthful foods. If we do not give our soil the proper rest and treatment so that minerals can become a part of the earth again, this world is doomed, and mankind will go down the drain by the end of this century. About the only place left for us to find good foods with minerals and herbs is the ocean floor. This has become a reservoir of accumulated wealth in chemical materials which makes the resources of the land appear as nothing in comparison.

Kelp is also used in cases of obesity, poor digestion, and obstinate constipation. It has a beneficial effect upon the reproductive organs, and a normalizing action upon the thyroid, sensory nerves, meninges, arteries, pylorus, colon, liver, gall bladder, pancreas, bile ducts, and the kidneys. Few singular plants have such a wide range of action on illnesses of the body and diseased organs.

Kelp has been reduced to a high potency tablet form so that it is much easier to handle. Many health authorities advise kelp for indigestion. A bottle of this valued seaweed should be kept on the medicine shelf at all times in order to relieve chronic constipation and stomach disorders and to act as an arterial cleansing agent giving tone to the walls of the blood vessels. Kelp is helpful in cases of arterial tension due to high blood pressure and in keeping down a host of disorders.

*Licorice* is an herb of which there are several varieties. Its name is a corruption of the Greek words sweet and root. It is one of the oldest and best known remedies for coughs and chest complaints. The knowledge and use of it dates back to the time of the early days of Egyptian civilization. According to some historians the early clay tablets found on the plains of Mesopotamia, which is supposedly the birthplace of civilization, gave many uses of licorice as a medicine and as the elixir of life.

The Hindus, Greeks, Romans, Babylonians, and Chinese all knew about the value of licorice. Gopal Das, one of the ancient ECK Masters, was responsible for it being introduced into Egypt for medical purposes.

It is a perennial herb which grows in most temperate countries. It is about two to five feet high with long, smooth green leaves and yellowish white or purplish flowers. The root is light brown with a sweet taste, fifty times the sweetness of cane sugar. It is a demulcent, expectorant, and laxative.

Its roots penetrate deeply into the ground and contain an abundance of valuable properties. It is a native of Greece, Asia Minor, Spain, Southern Italy, Syria, Iraq, Caucasian and Transcaspian Russia, Northern China, Persia, and North Africa.

Tons of licorice are used by all countries today for foods, medicines, beverages, confections, etc. The United States imports about fifty million pounds of licorice root and about half that amount of the liquid extract yearly. The root comes mainly from Iraq, Turkey, Russia, Syria, Italy, and British East Africa. The extract is imported mostly from Spain.

Some of the licorice extract entering the United States is used by the drug industries and made into various medications because of its demulcent and expectorant properties. The root, made into a powder, is often used in the preparation of pills. The extract has almost replaced the powder as a remedial agent.

Much of the supply of licorice is used by the tobacco industry as a conditioning and flavoring agent and by the confectionery industry as a base for a wide variety of candies. The residual material after extraction is used as a stabilizer in the production of foam fire-extinguishers and as a fertilizer for mushrooms.

The Chinese herbalists regard licorice as a healing agent either by itself or as an ingredient in various herbal formulas. It is also used to flavor beer and ale, ice creams, and as licorice water, which is a blood purifier.

The popularity of licorice as a remedy for coughs and chest complaints goes back to the remote ages. Witch doctors, priests, healers, and physicians of the various ages of history found in the licorice root something which would alleviate man's suffering. Each utilized the hidden powers of the root of this wonder herb as a curative agent in many different types of ailments.

It has been effectively used for centuries, not only in treating conditions such as tuberculosis, coughs, hoarseness, wheezing and shortness of breath, but it has also been found to be helpful for dropsy, constipation, fever, and as a blood purifier.

Licorice water was a popular drink in Egypt during the ancient days. The youthful Pharaoh Tutankhamen, who died in 1345 B.C., was buried with a supply of licorice root to help him on his last, long journey. It was a very popular therapeutic sweet drink for all the natives of those times. It was mostly imported from the fertile plains of Mesopotamia. It was also listed among the hundreds of drugs known during the Hammurabi reign of Babylonia.

Alexander the Great, so history says, distributed the licorice root among his own troops for medical purposes, just as a modern soldier carries his own first aid supply in campaigns. The Roman Legionnaires also considered licorice an indispensable ration for their grueling campaigns on the Roman frontiers. The Buddhists later adopted it as a sacred symbol for their ceremonies and rituals.

Almost anywhere one looks in man's history, licorice has been a part of the development of the culture and civilization of various nations.

Another wonder herb is *alfalfa.* Many believe that alfalfa is only fodder for animals. It is mainly a leguminous plant, much like peas and beans; however, the leaves and sprouts are eaten rather than the seeds alone. Alfalfa was one of the first known herbs, perhaps used over two thousand years ago. The Arabs discovered its valuable properties and called it the father of all foods. It has been only recently that we have rediscovered its valuable nutritive uses.

Alfalfa is a rich source of potassium, magnesium, phosphorus, and calcium, as well as all the known vitamins—including Vitamin K, and the recently discovered Vitamin B-8 and Vitamin P.P. Alfalfa is one of the richest known sources of organic salts. The depth and spread of its roots gives it an opportunity to absorb the valuable nourishment from the soil.

Alfalfa is a good remedy for blood pressure, for it contains all the necessary elements for softening hard arteries. Its rich iron content renders it a specific remedy for anemia, and its calcium content prevents dental problems. Many who are looking for youth and longevity would probably find it in the tea made from the dried green leaves of this wonder herb. It is sometimes called Lucerne in England and South American countries, and Buffalo herb in some parts of this country.

Alfalfa is believed to have originated in southwestern Asia, and historical accounts show it was first cultivated in Persia, now the country of Iran. From Persia it was taken to Greece during 500 B.C. and to Spain in 800 A.D. The Spaniards brought it to North and South America. In 1854 alfalfa was taken to San Francisco from Chile and from there spread rapidly over the western states.

Alfalfa is rich in proteins, minerals, and vitamins. Because the root extends as deep as thirty feet into the soil, alfalfa can reach stores of plant food. In sections of limited rainfall, alfalfa can withstand extremes of drought.

The plant is remarkably adaptable to various climatic conditions, but it is exacting as to soil conditions and proper sowing. The effect of alfalfa on irrigated land is to increase the value per acre of subsequent crops. Alfalfa is used as a soiling crop and as pasturage. In the form of silage, alfalfa hay is fed to dairy cows, beef cattle, sheep, hogs, horses, and poultry. It is also an excellent honey crop for bees and is used to increase the vitamin content of prepared foods.

Alfalfa production in the United States averages over eighty-five million tons a year. The most important alfalfa producing states are California, Idaho, Washington, South Dakota, Kansas and Nebraska.

It has been found that the green leaf of the alfalfa contains eight essential enzymes. They are lipase, a fat splitting enzyme, amylase, which acts upon starches; coagulase, which coagulates milk and clots blood; emulsin, which acts upon sugars, invertase, which converts cane sugar into dextrose; peroxidase, which is an oxidizing aid for the blood; pectinase, an enzyme that forms a vegetable jelly substance which aids digestion; and protase, which digests proteins.

Alfalfa serves as an aid to increase lagging appetites. There are enough minerals and enzymes in alfalfa, according to health authorities, to assist the digestion of all four classes of foods—proteins, fats, starches, and sugars.

Alfalfa as a human aid for health is on the shelves of most stores in the country. Alfalfa sprouts contain the vital, cell-building amino acids, such as phosphorus, chlorine, silicon, aluminum, calcium, iron, magnesium, sulphur, sodium and potassium in forms which the body can transform. It has been said that the alfalfa sprout contains over a hundred percent more protein than other grains. However, it is the chlorophyll contained in alfalfa which gives much of its healing quality for the body tissues.

The sprouts have calcium which would keep the teeth in good condition, as well as the heart and muscles. We find that alfalfa grown for human consumption is somewhat different from that which is cultivated for domestic animal use, as the fields are kept free from weeds.

*Hawthorn* is one of the wonder herbs used mainly in the treatment of heart diseases. It is also used as a diuretic, astringent, a tonic for sore throats, dropsy, and kidney troubles.

The hawthorn is a small tree belonging to the rose family. A native to the temperate regions, it is widely cultivated for its use as an herb. The hawthorn was regarded as sacred by the English country villagers during the Middle Ages, probably from the tradition that it furnished Christ's Crown of Thorns.

Hawthorn is called *Crataegus oxyacantha*, from the Greek *kratos*, which means hardness of wood; *oxus*, which is sharp; and *akantha* which is thorn. It attains a height of about thirty feet and lives to a great age. It passes a single seed-vessel to each blossom, producing a stony apple in miniature, and when ripe, is brilliant red. Throughout Europe, it is known as a very fine cardiac tonic and curative for organic and functional heart disorders. It goes by several different names—English Hawthorn, May Apple, Mayblossom, Whitethorn, Haw Tree, and Bread and Cheese Tree. Its fruit, which is bright red, has a yellow pulp that remains on the tree after the leaves drop in the fall of the year.

The hawthorn was used in ancient Greece as a marriage torch. In Rome it was considered a potent charm against sorcery and witchcraft. The leaves were put in cradles of the newly born babies to bring special blessings and protection. Greek brides often used sprigs of hawthorn, and the wedding altar was adorned with its blossoms to bring a blessed future for the bride and groom.

Hawthorn has now come under serious scientific research and it is reported to be used as a base for heart medicines. A liquid extract is made from the English hawthorn which has proven to be valuable in continued therapy for certain heart troubles.

The bush, or tree, has small serrated leaves and a profusion of tiny white flowers which later give way to meaty red berries called haws. During World War II, the berries were discovered to have a rich Vitamin C content by British Government research teams, and they were given to the troops to prevent scurvy and to guard against dropsy.

*Celery* has the Latin name of *Apium graveolens*. The seeds are used mainly in herbal remedies. Celery is good for rheumatism, gout, and as a carminative medicine for relieving gas and colic. Celery seeds are also used as a diuretic and a tonic for improving the muscular condition of the body, as well as an aid to promote restfulness and sleep. It is cultivated in most parts of the world for domestic use.

Celery has been known for its medicinal use for several thousand years. The ancients made good use of its benefits for distraught nerves.

The stalk is rich in potassium, sodium, calcium, iron, and Vitamin C. Celery is non-fattening and can be used as a nibbling food between meals for those who want to lose weight. Celery has the quality of satisfying hunger. The leaves of the celery plant contain vitamins A, B, and C, as well as potassium and sodium. The root contains potassium, sodium, calcium, iron, silicon, Vitamins A and B.

Celery is a biennial herb of the parsley family, a native of Europe, but it is grown widely throughout the world. The stalks often grow twelve to thirty inches high in cultivated varieties. The stalk is greenish in color and slightly bitter to the taste. Celery seed is used as a seasoning for soups and other foods. It is also used in the pharmacy as a sedative or to disguise the flavor of drugs. It is raised principally in California and Florida in the United States. Its production yearly is about twenty-five million crates, each weighing sixty-five pounds.

*Asparagus* is an herb of the lily family. It was used by the Romans and Greeks in ancient times and the young shoots were considered to be good food.

The common asparagus which grows best in rich, sandy soil, is a native of Europe and has now reached high proportions as a cultivated food in most countries of the world. The seeds are used as a substitute for coffee. It is raised principally in California and New Jersey in the United States. It is cultivated abroad in Southern Russia, Poland and Greece to a greater extent than in other foreign countries.

The root or seed is mainly used in herbal remedies. It is said to be a treatment for various heart conditions, dropsy, gravel in the kidneys and bladder or gall bladder ailments.

*Parsley* is common to our knowledge and raised nearly all over the world. It is a diuretic, carminative, tonic, aperient, and antispasmodic herb used for dropsy, cystitis, irritation, and inflammation of the kidneys and bladder, swollen glands and colic.

The ancient Greeks used it two thousand years ago. Galen, one of the first physicians known in history, wrote about its benefits. During the early Roman era it was used as a sweet food for audiences at public events, like moviegoers today purchase popcorn and other things to nibble on during a picture.

64

Today, parsley has a place in medicine as a basic ingredient to alleviate a wide number of complaints. Many use it in Europe for various medical reasons, but mainly it is used for its properties which are essential to oxygen metabolism and maintaining the general health of the body, especially the action of the adrenal and thyroid glands. Also, it is used for Vitamins A and C, which the plant contains in large amounts.

Another herb is *papaya*, a fruit of the tropical countries—especially the Americas. A native of Hawaii and the South Sea Islands, it has been brought to America where it grows well in the southern semi-tropical states and in the tropical Latin American countries.

It is a tree that grows several feet in height, producing a yellow melon with delicious soft inner flesh. Another species of the tree was grown in the tropics of the Central Americas and its fruit was used by the Incas, Mayans and other civilizations long before the Spaniards came to their shores.

The melon flesh is nature's finest digestant. It contains papain, an enzyme which has no equal. It will digest hard foods, is active in alkaline acid, and is of value as a neutral media. It also assists in the digestion of other foods and is a digestive aid for patients who have weak stomachs.

Papaya is a source of Vitamins A, B, C, and G, and is used in a good many types of preparations such as jams, marmalades, drinks, fruit salads.

The powerful protein digesting enzyme, papain, which resembles pepsin in its digestive action, is made into tablets and sold as an aid for protein digestion, especially for older people whose bodies have declined to the point where the stomach will not digest certain foods. It is also valuable as an active blood clotting agent and to arrest bleeding. Papain is also effective in destroying intestinal worms.

We also find protein digesting enzymes in the *pineapple*. Bromelin, similar to papain, gives valuable aid in helping to digest proteins in the stomach. It can also be found in the canned pineapple, so I am told.

Another herb which has valued use is *peppermint*. It is a part of the mint family such as spearmint and horsemint, which are found throughout Europe, North Africa, and Asia Minor. All of these have been popular herbs since the earliest of times and have been mentioned in many of the ancient writings.

Peppermint is grown commercially in North America, Europe, and parts of Asia. Most of it in the United States is raised in the Pacific Northwest and in the Mid-Western sections.

It is a perennial herb, has a square stem and aromatic leaves, with oil glands in the leaves while the stems secrete an aromatic oil. Other members of the same family are the Balm, Bugle, Calamint, Dragonhead, Horehound, Hyssop, Marjoram, Sage, Skullcap, and Thyme, to name a few.

Peppermint is the best known and it is used in flavoring beverages, jellies, sauces. It is used in herbal remedies for a wide variety of things, such as nausea, diarrhea, colic, nervous headaches. In medicinal purposes it is classed as antispasmodic and carminative.

The whole mint family has been used in some manner or other by the magicians, priests, and physicians for thousands of years.

There are many other herbs that will be taken up in other chapters which could be classified as wonder herbs, but those we have just discussed are the better known ones and are good, all-around conditioners for man's health.

## Chapter Five

## THE LIFE-GIVING
## PROPERTIES OF SEEDS

Those who follow the path of ECKANKAR, the
Ancient Science of Soul Travel, are conscious of just
where herbology fits into the spiritual works. It is
true that those who have learned Soul Travel—that is,
the movement of the inner consciousness through the
lower states of life into the ecstatic states and
awareness of God—can have pure freedom. But there
are many within the ranks of ECKANKAR who are
passing through the first stages of spiritual
unfoldment and need some physical assistance for the
body and mind.

The majority of people do not understand the laws
of this physical universe and believe that they may
well do as they like for years, only to learn one day
that a price must be paid for violating the laws of
good health. Not many can live like the ancient
adepts of the mystical order in ECK known as the
Order of the Vairagi.

The adepts live in the Himalayan Mountains along
the Tibetan border. Among them, Rebazar Tarzs, the
great ECK spiritual Master, is said by many to be over
five hundred years old. Many of the other adepts of
this mysterious order are beyond the normal age of
man.

Many of these adepts live in the spiritual city of
Agam Des. Few go to this strange place for they must
visit only by invitation and then in the Atma body.
ECKANKAR was brought here from Venus by an

unknown race which is living in Agam Des, and whom we know as the *Eshwar Khanewale*, or simply as the God Eaters. These beings are the members of the ancient brotherhood or Order of the Vairagi. They attained their name, the God Eaters, from the fact that they absorb cosmic energies instead of assimilating plants and other foods.

They have an extreme longevity, like the patriarchs of the Old Testament, and in some cases even longer. However, those living in the physical body should not try to develop themselves to this extent, for herbs, medicines, and other means of handling health must be done through the usual channels. Herbs are the aids that one obtains when he cannot be healed otherwise because of a Karmic condition. The medicine, health practitioner, and the family physician are part of maintaining good health on this plane.

So many people in desperation seek psychic and spiritual healing or go to famed spots like Lourdes to regain their health. Many are vastly disappointed and cannot understand why one person is able to come away completely cured and another does not meet with any success at all.

The whole crux of the problem is that it is a matter of survival with the individual. If a person has a good survival factor—basic personal traits such as cheerfulness, a reasonable amount of happiness in his disposition, a positive outlook on life and its problems and is kept busy most of the time—he is likely to have good health. Even during those times when he is struck with illnesses they are only temporary because of the nature of his disposition, which is good for his survival.

Too many persons look to spiritual healing for their health. To be frank with the reader, not everybody is able to have spiritual healing, regardless of what may be said about the many cases on record of those who have been healed. If one is high enough on the spiritual ladder there is little doubt about his receiving a healing when he makes a request. But our concern at the present is for those who are unable to get any degree of health returned at this particular stage except through the regular channels of herbs, medicines, and chemistry.

This brings us to the point of seeds and what benefit they might afford the health seeker. It appears that the primitives used seeds instead of meat for centuries. The reason for this was that it was easier to store seeds for the wintry months when the hunters were kept in their lodges and caves by inclement weather.

These tribes also found that it was less of an effort to gather up seeds and nuts than to hunt down animals for food. Sometimes hunting became too dangerous and some hunters never returned. It was also discovered that some seeds had a higher protein content than meat, and while the tribesman could not figure this out scientifically, he knew that there was something in the nature of seeds and nuts that made him feel just as well as when he ate meat.

Take, for example, Lecithin. Its contents are of much value to the human body for it contains a combination of fats, phosphorus, and nitrogen which forms an important part of the nerves of the brain. Most seeds provide a source of fats which do not cause cholesterol deposits. The Indians of the highlands in Central America have a high regard for the native squash and pumpkin seeds as protein, but if they were asked why they probably could not say.

The Japanese use sesame seeds for making meal for cooking. The Turks, Syrians, and Egyptians do the same, while in Spain and Portugal we find that acorns (oak tree seeds) are cultivated for their delicacy. The Turks also use the hemp seed, and the Hindus and Russians eat cucumber and sunflower seeds instead of candy.

The seed is one of God's gifts to man, for it

contains all the nutrients required for health and strength in the body. Yet it has been only a few years since we believed that seeds were something other than food for animals and birds.

Sprouted seeds are a valued raw food which we have been neglecting all these years. They have an exceptional richness in vitamins, including plant hormones which stimulate the endocrine glands. We find that the Orientals, especially the Chinese and Hindus, are great users of sprouted seeds.

At the present there are hundreds of farms in this country that are devoted entirely to seed production for human consumption.

Before the relatively current interest in the nutritional value of seeds, farmers kept their seeds, like the pumpkin and others, in order to replant and grow another crop. All they were interested in was the flesh of the pumpkin to feed families. Yet today we find seed farms practically everywhere, and seed companies that specialize in this particular market. It is interesting how the seed market has developed over these many years.

Live seeds and grain have been found in Egyptian burial tombs several thousand years old. Seeds, with their durable skin or covering, their insulated protection, may be preserved for a greater length of time than most herbs and plants.

Seeds, especially those of the cereal plants, form the greater part of the food for mankind. As early farmers spread north, south, east, and west from their native lands to countries where they found better lands for crops, new ideas were developed. Rye grew at low levels in Asia, but had a better yield in the uplands. In the same manner, oats and rye displaced wheat in Northern Europe. Meanwhile, different millets started growing in Abyssinia and in Northern China, where wild rice was developed. The latter spread southward and finally was to become part of the cultivated crops of the valley of the Ganges, the Southeast Asian countries, and Southern China.

Pungent and aromatic seeds have been used for many purposes in the past as well as the present. The coriander seeds were used by the Israelites at the feast of the Passover. They were also highly esteemed by Hindus, Arabs, and Egyptians. Caraway seeds have been used for centuries as a flavoring in cookery, baked fruits, or breads and cakes to give them relish. Fenugreek seeds are used as a condiment in Egypt and for curries in India. The natives of India also use Fenugreek seed for making a gruel with sugar and milk.

Hemp seed was used in the Middle Ages as a charm, but today it is put to better use as bird seed, and its oil in the manufacture of perfumes. Fennel seeds were used by the Romans for making the taste of medicines more pleasant. Today the seed is used in stock for soups and other cooking, as well as to flavor absinthe and liqueurs.

Mustard is one of the oldest seeds that we know, and has been of nutritional value since the early days of man. It is a pungent herb of the pepper order, and plants are cultivated for their seed. There are several types of mustard plant, but the commercial mustard which we find on the kitchen shelf for cookery is the black mustard plant. It is the plant from which the seeds are used for table mustard. Powdered mustard, which is a condiment, is also used as a medicinal substance. Powdered mustard seed is sometimes given by physicians as a powerful emetic. The mustard seed is often used for its rubefacient and counterirritant effect in the form of plasters.

Anise is valued as a diuretic, carminative, and pectoral. It is a plant which has an erect stem, branching from twelve to fourteen inches high, pithy, striated, and angular. Its petals are white. It was originally a native of Egypt, Syria, and the nearby islands of the eastern Mediterranean Sea. However, it

71

has become a domestic plant and has been raised abundantly on farms and in gardens throughout the world.

Anise is used for flavoring candies and medicine. It forms one of the bases for the common cough drop sold commercially. It is a little seed with much flavor which has been used as a basic ingredient from ancient times until the 17th century, when many new flavors began to be made from it. Anise has many uses for medicinal purposes, such as bronchitis and asthma. It is used as a flavoring in curry powder, cheese, cookies, sweet pickles, and liqueurs. Its oil, besides being used for masking the taste of unpleasant medicines and to perfume toilet articles, makes a useful ointment against lice and insects. Also, the oil is often used as a lure for fish bait and trapping small animals.

Senna pods are often used for medicinal purposes. It is a small shrub found to have originated in Egypt, Nubia, and Arabia. The early Arab and Greek physicians were among the first to use the pods of this plant as medicine. Most of the pods useful medicinally are from overseas plants. The American variety, for some reason, does not have any value for botanical and medical uses.

The seeds of the Privet plant are used in lotions to clean sores and ulcers. The Dog Rose is another plant of the wild rose family, whose seeds are used for bladder and kidney problems, and the pulp made into a delicious jam. White Acacia has a seed which contains an antibiotic substance similar to penicillin. The common ash and honey locust seeds also contain a similar penicillin-like substance.

Wild carrot seeds are used for colic, dropsy, and kidney stones.

Annatto is a bush which grows in the tropical areas of America. Its seeds are used to color butter, cheese, soups, rice, cosmetics, pomades, soaps, silks, varnishes. The seeds are said to be a source of Vitamins A and D.

The Betel Nut is widely known as a seed which the natives of Southeast Asia chew. Mixed with honey, syrup, or butter betel nuts are used in veterinary medicine as a vermifuge.

Cardamon is a member of the ginger family, native to the Oriental countries. Its seeds are used for curry powders, flavoring foods, incense and perfumes.

Pumpkin seeds have a good many uses. In China these seeds are a symbol of health. It is believed that they are valuable for medicinal purposes. It is said they have a vitalizing effect on the prostate glands. Pumpkin seeds contain an abundance of the B Vitamins, with smaller amounts of Vitamin A, as well as calcium and protein.

Clary seeds are made into a tea which is good for weak backs.

Fennel seeds are used for flavoring soups and boiled fish. The ancients believed that by eating fennel and using its seeds for flavoring, they gained strength, courage, and longevity. Now fennel is used mainly for purgatives, stomach ache in infants, and similar complaints.

Cumin seed is mentioned in the ancient sacred writings and by the early Greek authors. It was a popular household medicine and was also used as a spice during the Middle Ages. Cumin is still used as a condiment in Europe to flavor foods such as bread, soup, rice, pickles, cheese, curry powders. It is an aid for digestion, helps with colic and some types of headaches.

Fenugreek seed was popular with the old Mediterranean civilizations. The seed contains phosphates, lecithin, and iron. It is sometimes used as a substitute for codfish oil in treatment of rickets and anemia. It is also used as a food for horses and cattle.

Flax seeds are also useful, having numerous medicinal and economic uses. Flax is used in the base preparations of cough medicines, dysentery, catarrh, and in inflammation of lungs, intestines, and urinary passages.

Guarana is an herb which comes from the Amazon jungles. Its seeds are used by the Amazon Indians to pound into meal. A tea can also be made from the seeds. It is good for furnishing protein and keeping up strength of the body.

Psyllium is a common weed in Southern Europe. Its seeds have been used for centuries as laxatives, and sometimes as poultices.

The parsnip plant has a seed which is good for cirrhosis of the liver.

Sumach seeds, when beaten into a powder, stop hemorrhages and purgings.

The sesame seed is a native herb of India, but it is domesticated and now grown in all parts of the world. It is an annual plant, grown from Egypt to Japan for the sake of its seeds, which yield what is known as gingili oil. This oil is used in cooking, for lighting and lubrication. It is not odorous, has a sweet taste, and will keep for years without becoming rancid. The sesame is sometimes called tilseed.

The sesame plant grows to a height of about three feet and bears yellow or pink flowers. The seeds are eaten as food, and its pale yellow emollient oil is also used for anointing the body and hair in some religious ceremonies. The seeds of the sesame plant have always been favored by the ECK Masters for they are rich in vitamins, minerals, and proteins. They also contain an abundance of calcium and lecithin.

Sesame seeds are often used in India for the treatment of piles, constipation, and other intestinal troubles. The oil is used in the manufacture of margarine. It is sometimes ground and mixed as a paste-like substance which is used as a spread on bread, rolls, biscuits, and cookies. It is also used extensively in cooking, in products for commercial sales such as salad oils, and in the preparation of cosmetics.

Believed to be a native of the Sunda Island in India, the sesame plant has come a long way in the history of man, for today there are factory plants for processing the seeds in Ecuador, Mexico, Peru, Nicaragua, and Costa Rica. The use of sesame in this country was developed and promoted by the natural food business. Sesame has now become a household staple, for it is a valuable aid to the human diet.

Along with milk, meat, eggs, cheese, and nuts we find that seeds are our chief protein foods. It is here we learn that sesame seeds are similar to almonds in their composition, being an excellent protein food in methionine, which is effective for liver complaints.

Sunflower seeds are rapidly becoming one of the staples in the diets of America. They have been the staple food in the Balkan countries for many years, and since we have adopted the sunflower seed for eating purposes, it appears that general health has improved. The seed is extremely rich in methionine, and provides more of amino acids than liver.

The Greeks and ancient Romans were great enthusiasts for sunflower seeds. When the early French explorers made trips along the shores of the Great Lakes, they found the Indian tribes cultivating the sunflower for its seeds. When the Spaniards came to the shores of tropical America, they found the natives in Peru and Mexico harvesting the sunflower. The sunflower is grown in Russia today and its seeds are used as food. Oil cakes are made from the sunflower seed and used as fodder for cattle and horses during the cold Russian winter when food is scarce.

Sunflower seeds contain valuable nutritional elements. Its oil is excellent for use in salads and cooking. Research shows that the seed oil is an excellent aid in reducing the cholsterol level in the blood. The seeds contain an abundance of vitamins and minerals, are rich in Vitamin B complex, and supply an excellent source of protein. They also contain Vitamin A and a high content of phosphorus and calcium. The oil is used as an herbal remedy for bronchitis and as an aid for healthy eyes.

Processed sugar robs the body of Vitamin B which is so important to good health. The portion destroyed, so it is said, is thiamine, one of the basic ingredients for good health. Thiamine is the element of Vitamin B that aids with digestion and the assimilation of sugars and starches. Carbohydrates, sugars and starches eaten in their natural form, do not have the same effect on the body, for the thiamine can readily digest sugar or starch present in natural food.

Many historical characters have been greatly addicted to sweets—Hitler, Napoleon, Queen Elizabeth I, Alexander the Great, Stalin, Julius Caesar, Queen Victoria, to name a few. It does seem likely that the rulers named subjected themselves to the metabolic paradox of creating a condition of low blood sugar by eating too much sugar.

If the diet is balanced then we should have little worry about the problem of good health. Sugar is necessary, but not at the expense of other needs of the body. An excess of sugar in the blood stimulates the pancreas to produce so much insulin that not only is the excess removed from the bloodstream, but practically all the blood glucose as well. Insufficient glucose is left in the blood for the demands of what is needed by the brain cells. As a result, suspicion, depression, inability to think clearly, and anger become the effects in the individual whose intake of sweets is too high. He becomes somewhat indifferent, and he reaches a state in which he becomes cruel to others, sadistic in manner and thought, and his deeds are often marked by outstanding errors of judgment.

The most famous vegetarian of our times was Adolf Hitler. In order to compensate for the lack of zest in his diet, which was likely due to lack of meat protein, he went to extremes with sweets. This seems to be a somewhat common problem with vegetarians generally. A visit to any vegetarian restaurant will show all sorts of sweets, cakes, and pastries on the menu. Of course, many of these rich foods are made from whole grains, natural sugars, and such, but at the same time, many of them are not. Some who can be called "amateur vegetarians" ruin their health by trying to eat in this manner, and they learn sooner or later than a strict schedule does not work for their health. The races of people who have had to be vegetarians have been more warlike and have had more problems internally than those who maintained balanced nutrition per family within their respective countries.

It is not, in my opinion, that one way of eating is better than the other, but that each of us must find what is best for his own particular needs.

It appears that those persons who are reared in a home where the conditions do not warrant too many sweets, including candies and sugarized soft drinks, have a greater chance of being happier with an opportunity for longevity.

Perhaps the cause of the rise of crime today could be traced to this particular lack of good nutrition. At least some of it might, for many people apparently want only what the pleasure principle within them demands, and this is certainly true in the line of nutrition. If left alone, most people would take alcohol, sugared drinks, candies, pies, pastries, and cakes as their main food element.

It is noted that Denmark, which has the highest suicide rate in the world, has an average yearly intake of one hundred twenty-four pounds of sugar per person. What does this mean? Are the people having problems due to an over amount of sweets in their diets? It is a matter to be considered. The United States has an intake per person per annum of some one hundred pounds.

It is said that artificial sweeteners are able to give

the same effect upon the blood in the body as refined sugar. If this is anywhere near being true then anyone with a sweet tooth had best learn to discipline this habit, rather than succumbing to the problems it might bring. Try the natural sugars which come from honey and pure cane sugar, or fresh fruits. In any case, one would be far better off by eating fruits, which are freshly picked, than by trying pies, desserts, and other sweets.

The vegetarian who is motivated by a religious creed takes his stand on the moral issue that eating flesh is against the principles of spirituality. Anyone who is a chela of ECKANKAR knows that after he has become efficient in Soul Travel and can go into the fifth (Soul) plane, there is no right and no wrong, no beauty and no ugliness—only the one reality. Those who believe that vegetarianism is an asset to their spiritual growth are mistaken about the moral issue. However, there is an agreement that one might feel better if he were a very light eater of animal flesh.

If one is going to follow the path of the vegetarian, he would best examine his own physical makeup and learn if he is able to do so. It is the same in regard to fasting. Not everybody can fast, for it is not within the chemical makeup of their physical being to do so. Those who can, usually are sensible about the matter and attempt it a little at a time in order to harden their bodies so they can get used to whatever suffering they might encounter at the beginning of the fast. They usually fast a few days in the beginning, then wait a few days or weeks before going longer. In this manner they work up the strength and psychological preparation which must always go with a fast of any duration.

Fasting is as old as the human race. When nature did not provide a fast by droughts or floods, a religious fast was likely to take place.

The first things we must learn are the laws of

biology, which are actually the fundamental principles of the nature of *Kal*, the negative force. Man is subject to the trials and processes of evolutionary spiritual growth in his struggle for existence and survival. If we seem to escape trials it is because the group to which we belong has protected us, or because we, as chelas of ECKANKAR, have been surrounded by the Living ECK Master's love which wards off certain trials. He will take care of all his chelas up to a point, allowing them the lesson of some experience which is unique to each individual to undo some Karma.

The first thing that man learns is that life is competitive. When life is peaceful, food is plentiful; when life is violent, food becomes scarce and man looks for anything to eat. Animals eat one another without qualm; civilized men consume one another by due process of law. When men cooperate, there is an increase of social development, but this, too, is a tool and a form of competition. War is a nation's way of eating, but it promotes cooperation, because it is the ultimate form of competition.

Man will eat in some form or another—whether it is the devouring of one as a result of his appetite to satisfy a hunger, or being a member of a group that declares war on another. As long as man is in the physical body and living in the human state of consciousness, he is in competition with others and must do something to survive.

This is why fasting should be done voluntarily with the idea in mind that it is for spiritual growth and bodily health. If anyone fasts for any other reason, such as to force someone or some group into accepting his ideas or making changes, he has only made Karma for himself. This is poor Karma, indeed, for he must live through other lives in order to overcome that which he has forced another to do. Force in any form will not work, whether it be by fasting to change others, or by employing weapons, propaganda, and force of ideas.

Fasting in ancient times was necessary for some religions. It appears that this was a part of the spiritual growth of people who were seeking God. To tell anyone today to fast for any length of time would be like taking their property away; few, if any, could abstain from food of any nature for one day. But again, this depends upon the individual's psychological makeup and his physical endurance. There have been studies made of fasting in health circles and varied systems and ideas have been developed.

The complete or partial fast will free the body from any physical blockage that might be bothering it. When food is withheld the body starts feeding on itself from within. The inner healer takes over, and what is least essential to the body is used or released in some manner.

The first two or three days of the fast are the hardest. After that, most hunger pangs disappear and the individual seems to be free of any disagreeable feelings in the stomach and body. If one is not used to fasting, he should try only two or three days at first, and he should have the advice of the family physician or health authority before attempting it. If he should later feel that his endurance can manage a longer fast, then he can try whatever seems possible. He should not attempt the thirty day fast, which was part of the development of the spiritual giants, however. There is too much misery in starting a fast of this nature, and too much disappointment if one has to stop within a few days after starting.

The Initiates of the Second Circle of ECKANKAR are requested to abstain from food each Friday. If unable to do this, they are given permission to take a partial fast, or one with fruit juices only. In cases of the elderly, or those who are unable to do this, it is requested that they have a mental fast for this day, that is, to keep all thinking and action of a positive nature.

Chapter Six

## HERBS AND KARMIC
## CONDITIONS OF MAN

Many fashions are forming different faces for society. None of these are "revolutions," as the journalistic jingo tags them, but merely fads, which crop up from time to time in any social order.

The only real revolution is the enlightenment of the mind and unfoldment of Soul for spiritual growth, and the only real emancipation is Soul. Therefore, the only real revolutionists are the adepts of the ancient Order of Vairagi, the Masters of ECKANKAR. They are the ones who have had a secret influence on world history since the beginning of time. They are the ones who have gradually guided men through the ages, teaching them how to have social relationships with one another and how to promote a universal benefit for the good of all civilizations.

Within this overall pattern of life there has been the gradual discovery of herbs and their beneficial effect upon the human body. Man could not be given knowledge of all things at his beginning on earth. If he did have this knowledge, there would be little purpose for his being here. Man constantly looks outward to find the answers to life's problems. He fails to look inward, to the subjective inner life, the center where the SUGMAD dwells, or God as IT is known to the material world.

There are five lower planes, the physical, astral, causal, mental and subconscious. The Soul plane, which is the fifth, is the dividing line between the lower planes and the higher worlds. These lower planes were established for the benefit of educating Soul as to its divine origin. After many incarnations and participation in all problems of life, including the gathering of Karma, good and bad, the resolution of much of it and the retaining of some of it, Soul comes to the stage of its spiritual unfoldment where it meets the ECK Master, who assists it in self-realization and reasons for its being here on earth. When an individual receives the initiation from the Master, then all Karmic conditions start resolving and Soul will not have to return to this world again for rebirths. It has finished with the Wheel of the Eighty-Four, the circle of rebirths and deaths.

What has this got to do with herbs? We must think about the type of body that one individual has in comparison with another and about keeping the varied types well. One learns to handle his own positivity, usefulness, and balance. He can gain control of himself when he learns whether his body is influenced by oxygen, nitrogen, hydrogen, carbon, manganese, magnesium, potassium, sodium, calcium, silicon, phosphorus, or a combination of any of these, such as calcium-carbon-sulphur. These minerals are found in herbs and plants. When one learns how to preserve minerals in vegetables and meats, then he begins to build and maintain good health. But we must think very carefully about the Karmic conditions of man and the relationship to herbs.

In the beginning I want to point out that zodiacal signs play an important part in the Karmic conditions of every individual. A wandering Soul making its way from birth to birth may be required to pass through each of the zodiacal signs, where he spends so many lives in each, working off the Karma which must be collected and resolved within every sign of the zodiacal wheel. This is called the Wheel of the Eighty-Four for the number of times one spends in each sign of the zodiac, going through different births.

One spends so many lacs in each sign. A lac is equivalent to one hundred thousand years. Each Soul will spend at least eighty-four lacs going around the zodiacal circle, an average of seven lacs in each sign. He must work out the Karmic conditions which come with each sign. Therefore, he would spend at least eight million, four hundred thousand lives in this universe before Soul would be purified—that is, perfected so that it can go on into the heavenly worlds.

Man has one way of breaking the Wheel of the Eighty-Four. That is finding the MAHANTA, the Living ECK Master, who will train him and eventually initiate him into the mysteries of ECKANKAR. When one has been initiated, most of his Karma will be broken and run off in his lifetime. He will have a straight path into the heavenly world and will never have to return to this material universe again.

Now we must think in terms of which herbs and plants are best for one who has Karmic conditions to run off. The various types must be brought into focus through their traits, which correlate with the signs of the zodiac.

When matched with the type of mineral required, we find the first is oxygen.

*Oxygen* people are those who are chemically adapted to the plants and herbs which have much oxygen in their nature. They generally have qualities of aggressiveness, practicality, positivity, and a great deal of confidence in themselves. They are usually dark-skinned, dark-eyed, broad-faced, solid and muscular. These people use a great deal of oxygen because of their physical and mental energies which require extra work for the heart, muscles, tissues, and cells.

On the nodules of growing legumes (peas, beans and clovers) are tiny, almost microscopic living organisms which have the power to change the chemical nature of plants and enable them to absorb nitrogen from the air and soil. These are called nitrobacteria and they actually draw oxygen from the air and provide the plants with nitrogenous or proteid matter. They also enrich the soil with nitrates and nitrites, two oxygen carriers. By attracting nitrogen, the nodules cause the potassium and sodium in the soil to take up oxygen and release it to the plants.

Nitrates carry three atoms of oxygen and one atom of nitrogen, while nitrites carry two atoms of oxygen and one atom of nitrogen. Without the action of these microscopic organisms, proteid and protein foods would be impossible.

The legume family (peas, beans and clovers) extract a specific group of minerals from the earth. These minerals are calcium, potassium, phosphorus, and sulphur.

Those who are of this oxygen nature have a Karma, which with too much indulgence in foods, especially rich diets, results in overweight, heart ailments, aggressiveness, vanity, attachment to material things, imperfect blood and kidney problems.

The *nitrogen type* is next. Nitrogen is an element of nature which is gaseous and serves as a diluting agent for oxygen. It is an important element in plant nutrition, for certain bacteria in the soil accomplish the conversion of atmospheric nitrogen to form such as nitrate, in which plants can absorb nitrogen. In the form of protein, nitrogen is a necessity to the tissues of the body.

This type has a tendency to be pessimistic. Even their appearance has this look about them, for they are heavy, stocky, dark in coloring, and usually wear frowns. Unfortunately, they have an intake of too much nitrogen from foods which tends to decrease the oxygen element's activity in the body, making them inactive and giving the look of laziness.

They have Karmic problems with the digestive tract and elimination; they tend to be overweight, slow in thought and motion and to suffer feelings of oppression when living in the city or crowded areas.

Nitrogen suppresses oxygen. Being protein in nature, the more of it consumed as heavy animal protein, the more oxygen is taken away. This is why those of this type must be very careful about their diet being balanced. For this reason it can be said again that, when we begin to break down categories of people, one person can be a vegetarian and another cannot. It is now that one can begin to see why he might have an affinity for another kind of food.

Not only are we dealing with individual types, but to national and racial groups, according to what their characteristics, habits and culture might be. History will bear this out.

Next is the *hydrogen type*. When hydrogen is missing in the body, the individual has flabby muscles and tissues. Combined with oxygen and nitrogen, hydrogen is one of the elements needed by the body to keep the muscles taut and in tone. Those who are of the hydrogen type are usually strong, muscular people who enjoy physical work and a large degree of exercise. They seldom tire, because they take their work or exercise passively and conserve their energies. This gives them the appearance of having great endurance and the ability to work long periods without resting. They are rotund, blue-eyed, brown-haired and large-headed.

The Karmic pattern of life here is the chance of losing a certain amount of vital energy, which could result in muscular tremors later in life. The hydrogen are types apt to have congestion of the lower intestines and bowels. There is also a tendency toward dropsy, heart weakness, and some respiratory troubles. The diet should be watched very carefully and kept more to the light, dry type of foods.

The next type is the *carbon category*. They are usually fleshy in body and spend most of their time trying to get out of work. Because they are indisposed to work, they become inactive and retiring, lacking fire because they have upset the chemical balance of their bodies by too many sweets and starches. This type is usually overweight and babyish looking.

If the individual cannot burn off the carbon in the body properly, he feels weak most of the time. The greater the consumption of carbon, the greater the need for oxygen. A small amount of oxygen and a great amount of carbon will result in a small burnoff of the latter and the result is weak and flabby muscles. The carbon people have poor bones, for carbon has a poor affinity for oxygen. They crave sugar, which is carbon for energy and heat, but they do not have enough oxygen intake to burn the carbon and produce muscle energy. Unless there is proper diet and sufficient exercise, they become lethargic and weak. Many carbon people have weak backs and spines, due to a lack of iron, poor digestive systems, and poor bones.

The *manganese type* generally have good minds, often very brilliant. They are slender with thin faces and prominent jaws. Their coloring is usually blondish or neutral, which gives them an old appearance. Manganese is needed in the body to overcome laziness, sterility, and marital weakness. It is also needed for nerve health, solid bone structure, good digestion, and general overall body utilization, as well as to build resistance against illness.

The manganese people are generally impatient, uncertain, disturbed by noise and clamor. They are highly nervous and prone to many errors and some accidents. They are apt to be very worrisome about even the most minute details. Sometimes they are unable to control their emotions, bursting into weeping or excessive laughter, even giggling, and sometimes a few will use violent language, which is shocking to themselves. They seem to lack a control within themselves, give way to things, then in reflection, wonder what happened. These are Karmic conditions which can be corrected by diet.

If manganese becomes balanced in their bodies, they will be likely to improve in their attitudes, their outlook on life, and be far happier in disposition. Their diet should consist of neutral foods such as pecans, olive oil, coconut, and eggs—plus the manganese foods, which are blueberries, lettuce, pineapple, wheat and bran cereals.

The *magnesium type* is highly restless, muscular, somewhat heavy, with dark brown hair and a flexible body, even to the extent of being "double-jointed." The magnesium people need a good vegetable, fruit and nut diet, which should be offset by sea foods and lean beef. They need both magnesium and calcium in their diet. Occasionally, those of this type are not at all interested in close relations with others, which is a state of emotional instability sometimes seen.

This is part of the Karmic pattern which one must go through if he is this type of person. However, this Karma is not entirely without some sort of resolution, provided he places himself under the proper health authorities or his family physician, who has knowledge of the various categories of persons. Of course, there is always the chance that one will try to analyze himself according to these different types and this would be a mistake. Few people have the insight to look into themselves and see what is wrong. They need the experts to do this, and if at all possible, they should go to a reliable health counselor and not call upon every psychic or fortune-teller in the telephone book. Although psychics may have the ability to say what is wrong, they do not have the authority to pronounce their findings.

The *potassium sort* of person is one who has greater recuperative powers than the others. However, if he has reached a low ebb of vitality and energy, he is liable to have periods of instability. These people are usually small or of medium height. They live better in domestic peacefulness, because they are naturally of a timid nature and are very serious.

If there is a lack of potassium balance in the body, this type of individual will suffer from pyorrhea and eye troubles. The potassium people usually have red or light-brown hair, affable dispositions, and full faces. They have an affectionate nature and a constant wish for family life.

The Karmic pattern here is one of hypertension, which may affect the heart, throat, nose, and sinuses. A person in this category generally has a cough which has been with him since childhood. His body is usually very thin with nerve weakness. Often his mind is in poor condition with no strong memory and an inability to handle complex details. These people usually are vegetarians or near-vegetarians. They get their potassium and calcium from fruit.

Often, if one is of this chemical nature, he will be extremely nervous and a great worrier. He will be moving about at night when others wish to sleep. This takes away his normal rest and makes him very susceptible to certain health problems.

The *sodium group* of people are more or less manual laborers. If not, they enjoy sports and other outdoor activities. They are usually hard workers and have stocky, muscular bodies.

Sodium acts upon the blood, secretions in the body, the membranes of the vital organs, including the throat and the alimentary canal. If there is not enough sodium in the body, the stomach walls will weaken and acidity will result, causing the person to lash out with a verbal storm and to become extremely sarcastic. The lack of sodium also causes mental depression.

Besides these points, there is a pattern of gallstones, throat trouble, bladder problems, slow elimination, slow recovery after an illness, and a tendency to overeat, which come from not having the proper diet.

The *calcium type* is usually slender with a large skeletal structure. He has a thin face, deep eyes, and his hair is usually brown. He is slow working in his actions, but he works hard at anything he must do. His expression is always intent and serious, but he is tenacious in nature, and he will finish a job regardless of the cost to himself or to his health.

He is stiff in his disposition, as well as in his body and limbs, because this is the nature of the calcium type. He will normally have longevity in life, but he should always be temperate in everything, including physical and mental labor. He is pretty good at a vegetarian diet, but he must have physical and emotional warmth in his life. He has trouble with his elimination because of his eating habits, and he should pay attention to a laxative diet consisting of foods that would help him in this area daily.

Because his disposition is generally serious and seldom changes, he can be expected to be gruff and direct in dealing with people. This is part of his Karma and must be expected of him. Unless one knows this, the calcium type can certainly upset one. It is most important that people understand one another—i.e. their chemical types—before entering into marriage. If more people did, there would be fewer separations and divorces in this world.

Too many people expect love to resolve their problems. Love is not the ultimate answer to the human element here in this physical world, but understanding is. Once we begin to understand and let compassion guide us, we are no longer in the hands of the *Kal* (the negative) forces.

Many do not understand that this negative force is very subtle, and it takes many turns and diverse means to keep us in its hands. Perhaps Socrates struck the keynote for defeating this negative force within ourselves by stating, "Man, know thyself." This is Truth, but we are so wrapped up in the astral and the materialistic forces which are the basis of the negative that it is seldom that we can attain Truth anywhere.

89

The *silicon people* are overactive people, for they must hurry and rush about doing all sorts of things, some perfectly useless and other things for good reasons. They are people with a certain amount of nimbleness, and they are constantly gay about all life.

Many of them are constant talkers, often boastful. They are quite wide-eyed, their hair is dark, sandy and light brown. The silicon people are good party-goers, for they are open and friendly; but their energies drive them so much that they seldom are good thinkers. Their most prominent feature is that their ears stand out from the head. They cannot do heavy work, and if they do, will generally collapse from exhaustion.

Their Karmic pattern is that their skin is very susceptible to the elements. They should rest often, because of a lack of energy, and most of all, they should take a rest from talking. They need natural sugars and salts. Silicon is found in onions, spinach, parsnips, pumpkins, strawberries, asparagus, celery, and lettuce. Silicon helps with the disposition. If the silicon type take care of their skin, which can develop malignancy, there is a good chance of these individuals living to a ripe old age.

The *phosphorus type* of person has a pear-shaped head when looked at from any angle. There is a mental alertness in the faces of the phosphorous people which shows a desire for reading, studying, and learning. Their hair is sort of brown, and their eyes are usually blue or grey. The neck is slender, often long, and the body is thin with narrow shoulders and broad hips.

These are people who literally shine in the dark. They can grasp ideas fast, but they do not have the stamina to put these ideas across. This is part of their Karma which has been brought over from past lives. They do not take care of their bodies and they eat little, thus making their bodies look fragile and delicate. The phosphorus people are the mind people, and they make good teachers, lecturers, and students of almost any subject their minds are put to handling. But they have the problem of a lack of balance of phosphorus. The body must have a normal intake of phosphorus to aid in calcium assimilation to maintain normal health.

The phosphorus people need a well-balanced diet, prescribed by someone who knows how to handle such problems. They also need a quiet atmosphere, recreation, and much sleep. They cannot take drugs and expect to be kept in good health. Their greatest Karma is the problem of thinking too much! They theorize, compare, imagine, analyze, speculate, and invent. This is good, but at the same time, it is not good when overdone, for it wears down body resistance to disease.

We are dealing in this chapter with astral circumstances and situations. These are the hidden factors of human existence and they must become part of the knowledge of all who are interested in knowing about themselves and in gaining spiritually.

The Karmic pattern of the individual is hardly anything more than astral and mental problems, especially astral activity, the feeling and grasping areas of something within one's self. In the thousands of years man has been on this earth, he has hardly gone any further than the astral plane in his advancement.

The astral is the plane of emotions. It is where the culture world exists, which includes the arts, painting, music, writing, and sculpturing. It is the plane of sentimental love, often mistaken for spiritual love. One has to take into consideration all of this when trying to work out some of his inner problems, especially when it is due to Karmic patterns of past lives.

The *sulphur type* people are handsome with golden, reddish or brown wavy hair. They have high foreheads and attractive smiles. Most of them are slender and talented in some artistic field, perhaps music, art, or writing. They are keenly interested in everything and very susceptible to luxuries, but their basic Karma is an explosive temperament, and they expect all people to forgive them immediately. This sort of temper is the cause of their skin troubles. A diet high in sulphur from raw foods so the contents would not change would assist in their temperamental, sensitive problems. They must also be careful of elimination conditions.

The *calcium-phosphorous* people are very delicate, refined, and extremely cultured. They have dark brown hair, slender necks, and somewhat poor vitality. Their heads are usually narrow and flat in the back at the point where the spine joins the head.

The phosphorus in this type is generally burned up by great mental activity, making them nervous people. Without enough phosphorus for the rest of the body, the other minerals cannot be assimilated and used. Therefore, the calcium needed for the bones is not available. A lack of exercise in this type, because they like to read so much, keeps the oxygen supply low, so that the potassium which is present in the diet cannot be used in the body. It is because of the potassium that iron becomes a part of the blood and without it the body becomes anemic, the person nervous and exhausted. This is part of the Karma with this type of person.

Since the blood is not purified because the supply of oxygen is not getting to it, weak circulation and poor digestion result. If one gets enough exercise, this situation in his health condition can be remedied. The calcium-phosphorus type also has a great need for vitamins and requires more calcium foods with which to combat anemia. Also, nerve foods should be in the diet such as raw eggs, coconut, and olives. This type of person should strike a balance between mental and physical exercise, get plenty of sunlight, take deep breathing exercises and body massage.

This type should be careful not to deplete himself of what energies he already has. Being overactive can leave him depleted and he should practice moderation in everything he does.

The last chemical category is called the *balanced type*. This is a combination of the calcium, carbon, and sulphur chemicals in the body. Calcium gives them strength of bones; carbon keeps the type congenial; and sulphur gives them a good appearance. The hair of this type is generally light-brown or reddish, or they may be blonde with blue eyes.

One of the Karmic patterns which they have is a weak digestion. They are thinkers who are active, as well as having good perception and insight into human nature. Reason, will, and logic all blend perfectly in this type. These are the ones who set their goal for success and wealth in this material world and succeed.

If the sulphur aspect is greater than the others, that is, if it is out of balance, these individuals will have tempers which can explode without rhyme or reason. They can, also, even though balanced, outrun their natural energies and become depleted and have a poor oxygen intake because of a lack of exercise.

The balanced type must have a plain diet for his daily fare. He cannot eat desserts, rich pastries, or candies. If he begins to fall off this daily fare then his health will start going down until he is unable to perform with efficiency.

One must begin to think about himself in terms of chemistry in his body according to minerals. Since one's pattern of life can be judged from his advent into this world, at least some knowledge should be given so that each person can understand himself a little better.

What we are today is, of course, what our Karma might be; but on the other hand, there are so many factors in life and so many aspects to reincarnation and Karma that it becomes nearly impossible to explain them to a lay reader. However, Karma is a matter which can be cleared up in a relatively reasonable time, provided any individual wants to be rid of the heavier problems which confront him. Much of it can be done through the right way of approaching body health, and in understanding the chemistry of the temple in which we each are enclosed in this world.

There will be arguments about this, and one of them is that if one has spiritually developed completely enough, none of these things are necessary. This is true, but how many spiritually developed people does one find in this world? How many come anywhere near the degree of perfection so designated by the religionists and true spiritual giants? There is only a handful in comparison to the masses of people who have lived in the body during the various ages.

For example, supposedly there are ten billion people who have lived on earth since the time of Tiberius Caesar, in whose reign Jesus lived and died. Of all these men and women who lived and died, nearly all have been forgotten. Only a few names remain on the pages of our history books. Of the names whom we know well, most of them are military conquerors, and perhaps, a handful of holy men, saviours, and mystics. Most of the latter died within a span of a few years, some by deliberate murder, others lived out a lifetime. But all we find here is that only a few can be considered above the average man in spiritual development, and yet, something took them away early in life. Perhaps it was calculated assassination, as in the case of Jesus, or an accidental death like that of Buddha, or old age in the case of Mohammed. There are others, but few have ever caught the secret of the key to good health, longevity, and spiritual perfection. These are the three desires held by every person who has any religious instinct apparent within himself.

Since these three aspects of life are the result of an order and procedure of spiritual enlightenment developed by God-Realization, it is not very likely that too many people are going to have them. But the fortunate ones do realize how they have been chosen to receive these gifts of God and are extremely thankful.

When we look at the lives of the ECK Masters, some of whom are beyond the age of normal man, it is amazing to try to understand what the meaning is in their long lives. These are Souls who have kept their original bodies on earth. The trio who are well known in ECKANKAR are Rebazar Tarzs, Fubbi Quantz, and Yaubl Sacabi. They are all retaining the original bodies which they took as Souls in this lifetime.

Rebazar Tarzs, the youngest, is said to be some five hundred years old. This would mean that he came into this life during the fifteenth century and still occupies the same body today. The purpose of his keeping the physical body is that he was the Living ECK Master for quite some time before passing the Rod of ECK Power to another. He still retains his body although he lives practically in seclusion in a remote section of the Hindu Kush Mountains. He was born in the western province of China, which is known today as the Chamdo area, on the border of Tibet.

Fubbi Quantz is the next oldest in the line of ECK Masters in the ancient Order of Vairagi, which is the order of these particular adepts. He is the head of the Katsupari Ashram in the Thanglha Mountains in Northern Tibet where he has charge of a number of persons who are studying the works of ECK. He is also in charge of the first section of the *Shariyat-Ki-Sugmad*, the sacred scriptures of the ECK Masters.

Heading the order of the ancient ECK Masters is

Yaubl Sacabi, who is the spiritual leader of the spiritual city of Agam Des, which is located in the remote crags of the western Himalayan Mountains in the same area as Kamet, one of the highest peaks in Northern India. It is located in the province of Uttar Pradesh on the Tibetan border and is one of the group of peaks which includes Nanda Devi. All are twenty-five thousand feet or more in elevation.

Few ever visit the spiritual city of Agam Des except by invitation. Its leader, Yaubl Sacabi, heads up the whole order of the ECK Masters on this planet and his age is beyond human conception. He lives in the physical body much of his time, as do some of those who are citizens of this spiritual community. They use the famed drill of the *Eshwar-Khanewale* (the God-Eaters) to maintain their health and strength in the human body. They are able to consume the Cosmic Spirit for food which preserves their bodies, enabling them to serve the inhabitants of the many planets in this universe. The second section of the *Shariyat-Ki-Sugmad*, located in the Temple of Golden Wisdom, is also under the guardianship of Yaubl Sacabi.

Anyone fortunate enough to learn rejuvenation methods, such as the *Ayur Vedha* system of renewing the body health, can look and feel thirty years younger. The *Kaya Kalp* treatment, which is a part of the *Ayur Vedha* method, is used mainly to bring back youth and health to anyone who is able to find it.

Before the Chinese invasion of Tibet, many of the Easterners who knew about the works of ECKANKAR, made pilgrimages to the Katsupari Ashram to undergo these youth and health treatments. Now the frontier has been blocked on the Tibetan border and few ever get across, unless they go the difficult way, risking life and limb, up through the mountain passes which have not yet been fully opened to traffic.

The ECK Masters may eat a little solid food in

public while in the presence of their followers—especially they will take bread, some meat and tea. They will not try to act differently in order to arouse the curiosity of the people around them nor to attract attention. In fact, they will keep public attention away from themselves as much as possible. This is why they are always inaccessible and cannot be reached by the public.

People long for the ECK Master and will try to touch his hand, be near him, and gather to themselves anything possible from him. They will try to see him merely for *darshan* (to receive a blessing by gazing upon his countenance). The ECK Master seldom gives thought to himself, his body, or to his needs here in the physical environment. Herbs, minerals, and plants are a natural part of the world which God has given man to keep his body healthy. The Living ECK Master will try in every way possible to attain and to increase his knowledge of all things, including health, nutrition, and foods for man in his journey to God.

Among the things which are frowned upon by the ECK Masters is sweet chocolate. It is not recommended for the body health, especially in the form of candy. Yet today most of the candies and sweets, including desserts, are made from a chocolate base. It is found to be hard on the digestive system and should not be eaten.

We must remember that the mineral rich person is a happy one and often very successful in his work. He radiates a personality so different and unusual that he is often admired instantly upon meeting him.

So many minerals of various types are needed by the body to provide health and the enjoyment of life and they should never be overlooked. Those who understand these needs and how minerals influence the body are indeed blessed, because they can have longevity, work out many of their Karmic problems and have a wonderful spiritual unfoldment.

Chapter Seven

## THE SACRED HERBS
## OF THE ANCIENT MYSTICS

More than a thousand years before the birth of Christ, a people known as the Shang or Yin lived along the Yellow River in North Central China. Very little is known about their origin and history but their civilization was very old and very rich. They left abundant evidence of great technical skill in casting bronze, in shaping pottery, and in fashioning the written words which are the direct ancestors of the modern Chinese characters. From the inscriptions on bone and bronze, the names of some of their kings and the nature of their divination are known.

However, the greatest body of knowledge which these ancients left was their understanding of herbs. They spoke about ginger and other herbs, which are known today among the average Chinese, but their finest contribution was the ginseng plant.

The ginseng grew wild in seclusion, hiding itself from man, seeking unfrequented deep shady forests and hillsides for its growth.

The taste of the ginseng is similar to that of licorice. The ancient Chinese developed it in accordance with their belief in its extraordinary virtue as an elixir of life. They used it as a remedy for many diseases, as well as for relief from the fatigue of the body and the mind. Today, the demand for the ginseng root in China is so great that large quantities are imported from other countries to keep up with the amount consumed by the Chinese people.

Ginseng is the common name for two species of

the *Panax* herb, which comes from the *Araliaceae* family. The root of this constitutes the drug which is supposedly good for many ailments and for general health in China. The *Panax Quinquefolius* is the American ginseng, which is a native plant of the cool woods of Quebec and Manitoba, ranging southward to Florida, Alabama, Louisiana, and Arkansas. There is a vast amount of ginseng cultivated in America, most of which is carefully dried and exported to Hong Kong. From there it is distributed throughout Southeast Asia and China.

The panax ginseng is native to Manchuria, Korea, and Japan. It is cultivated in large quantities there and sold throughout Asia, because it is often believed to be of a better quality than the American ginseng plant.

From time immemorial, the Chinese have believed that ginseng is a cure for all diseases and infirmities. Because of its slowness of growth, it takes about five to seven years for the ginseng plant to mature from seed to the full plant, and the cultivation of ginseng as a plant is often confined to an acre for growing. Not too many people are interested in a harvest unless the crops are rotated so that there will be one each year.

This brings about an interesting point in regard to the American type of ginseng. According to history, which forms the tradition of our mental thought from generation to generation, the discovery of America benefited only Spain. This is not true, for it was the discovery of new plants, herbs, and other types of products for food that revitalized Europe and the rest of the world.

The gold which poured out of the New World into the coffers of the Spanish kings was nothing in comparison to the nutritional wealth gained by the discovery of America. But at that time, few people, except for enterprising merchants, knew what was happening to their countries.

Christopher Columbus, who was a student of the ECK Master, Fubbi Quantz, was encouraged to take his sea voyage to the West. Fubbi Quantz knew what was in store for the navigator, and he was very anxious for Columbus to make a sea journey in order to open up the new worlds beyond the Atlantic.

Fubbi Quantz was traveling through Europe at the time, and he was greatly impressed by the nutritional poverty of that continent's people. They were protein poor, and they needed a flood of the right products in order to overcome this condition. He knew that it took too long for ships to sail around the Cape of Good Hope to bring food to Europe.

Therefore, Fubbi Quantz saw no other solution than to open the doors of the Americas where the real gold of the Indies was green products. From the new continent would come maize, the potato, the tomato, and legumes to ease the starvation diet of the European poor and to give them the protein needed for new energies. Man's life span in the fifteenth century was hardly beyond the age of thirty-five years.

The new varieties of beans would ease the fasting of the clergy, for the kind they had then were of the cattle food type, the poorest protein type which could be found. Even the poor of India had food somewhat better than the European clergymen.

The American herbs and plants would go far toward helping to abolish poverty and to make the population more stable. They would provide the human energy for the changes in history with the coming of the industrial revolution and the new age of urbanization, and would enable the farmers and peasants—a small fraction of the population—to provide food for the rest of the European nations.

Fubbi Quantz, in the interest of humanity, laid out the plans for Columbus one evening in Genoa, in a vision similar to the one which George Washington had at Valley Forge during the winter of 1778. It was then that Columbus began to make known his plans for finding a new trade route to the East. He finally came to the court ruled by Ferdinand and Isabella, who were in need of something to bolster their economy. Although Ferdinand was reluctant, the Queen aided Columbus to outfit a fleet for his explorations. The discovery of the western hemisphere, with all its green gold, changed the face of the world, although none realized this at the time.

The Chinese claimed that their sick took ginseng to recover their health, while those in good health used it to make themselves resistant to disease. It is said that it is common for many Chinese women over seventy years of age, who are users of ginseng, to have children.

It is believed that the first knowledge of the medicinal herbs was written by a monk, Shun-Chung Tsang, in about the year 3100 B.C. Fragments of this manuscript have been found and recorded. Ginseng was regarded as the highest among the many herbs which were then in use and was used as a tonic to strengthen the body, prolong life, invigorate the mind, and for helping the romance of the heart.

Other references to ginseng have been noted here and there in the Chinese writings. Marco Polo found it in great use when he traveled through China during the year 1274. After a study of it, he did not believe that ginseng rated much interest, and he never had much to say other than noting that it was widely used among the Chinese for practically everything.

The reason that the wild ginseng sells for a much higher price than the cultivated ginseng is because it is more potent and more difficult to secure. The belief that radioactive substances from the earth are more potent in ground where the ginseng grows also brings a better price for the wild plant. However, wild ginseng is more difficult to find, for it is believed that the ginseng plant is so sensitive that it will, at the slightest sound, fold its flowers and make itself look a great deal like other plants. Therefore, the hunter cannot readily detect it as he can other herbs and plants.

In Tibet ginseng is found especially in the northern areas where the natives gather the plants in the highlands. This is done during the early season of the year right after the snow has left the ground and flowers and plants are springing up in profusion. The monks from the monasteries and the natives seek out the ginseng plant in the dark hollows of the hills where it hides itself from human eyes.

It is strange that ginseng is so highly regarded by the Oriental countries while at the same time it is almost entirely ignored by the West. Western health authorities have apparently not found any use for the ginseng plant. At the same time, the Russians have been doing an enormous amount of scientific research in learning about the herb.

During World War II the Russian government had huge fields of ginseng growing in the wildest parts of the Sikhote-Alin Mountains. Here it was that Russia put several experimental stations and proved that the roots of the ginseng plant contained many radioactive properties. Now it is said that the Russians are still working with the plant in South Siberia, where large plantations of ginseng have been planted, at a cost of millions of dollars to the government. So far, they have kept their findings secret and are not letting the rest of the world know why they are going into such tremendous research on the ginseng plant.

It is believed that the action of ginseng on the endocrine glands gives the body the power to make better use of vitamins and minerals, which helps to overcome nutritional deficiencies. The Greeks believed that ginseng had magical virtues. The Japanese think of it as a longevity herb, and the American Indians used it for stomach disorders.

Another herb plant which has collected mysteries

and myths around itself is the mandrake. Its uses and influence are given in most occult literature. It was, and still is, one of the favorite plants of the magicians, for it is supposed to have powerful influences when used in magic spells and rituals.

The mandrake is sometimes known by its common names—May Apple, Raccoon Berry, Yellow Berry, Hog Apple, Duck's Foot, Wild Lemon, or the Indian Apple.

The leaves of the mandrake plant are dark green, hairy, and pointed; the flowers are white and the root is shaped like a parsnip, which is often forked, giving it an uncanny human-like shape. Medicinally, only the roots of the plant are used, and they are gathered late in October or early in November, soon after the plant has ripened.

The mandrake belongs to the barberry family. It is native to the temperate regions of East Asia and East North America. The flower is borne at the apex of the stem with six to nine petals, many stamens, and a solitary pistil. The fruit is a large, fleshy berry. It grows in the wet woods of East United States and East Canada, producing flowers in May which have yellow berries in July. Its roots are used in medicine, but they are poisonous in the raw stage.

In ancient times the plant was dedicated to Circe, the enchantress, who was celebrated for her witchcraft. Ulysses, the wanderer, had an unpleasant encounter with mandrake during his voyage homeward following the Trojan wars.

The fruit of the plant is like a golden apple, or globe. Therefore, it is often known as the love apple. The American Indians were well acquainted with the virtues of the plant, and modern physicians have recognized its value to the medical profession.

The mandrake herb is a somewhat drastic purgative found in the rich woods and thickets of North America and Canada. If it is carefully prepared and taken in small doses, it is one of the best herbs for cleansing the liver from foreign matter and stimulating it to action. It is not usually taken alone, but is combined with other less active laxatives, such as licorice, cascara, and other similar types of medicals; because alone, it has the effect of producing pain, contractions of the bowels, and distressing griping. Mandrake is modified in its action by adding some warming and stimulating herbs, such as ginger or cloves.

Mandrake is also of value, so say health authorities, in bilious and typhoid febrile diseases, for it acts as an emetic-cathartic which breaks up the disease. It is also said to be one of the best herb remedies for tropic liver, jaundice, and constipation. Mandrake should never be taken by anyone on their own, but only upon the advice of medical or health authorities, for as said before, it must be taken in small prescribed doses; otherwise it creates a great deal of pain and inflammation. Even in small doses there is liable to be some pain with taking it.

Books by the score could be written about the lore of the mandrake plant. To begin with, it is a root plant and the bane of many farmers, since it spreads like wildfire, deep underground. The foliage is seen in many states along hedges, ditches, trees. The plant can infest a whole field, and it is hard to get rid of because it is persistent and hardy in growth and strength.

Mandrake was used by the ancient sorcerers for love philtres, and it is mentioned in the *Old Testament* as an ingredient for love potions. In the Dark Ages it is said that the roots of the mandrake were a part of the concoction put into the witch's cauldron. In the Middle Ages, a concoction of the mandrake berries was used as an opiate, as well as a love potion. It could have had the dual effect of putting one person to sleep, while stimulating another. It was common knowledge that during the Middle Ages the mandrake was supposed to grow under the gallows of hanged men. Pulled from the earth, the root gave out wild shrieks, and those who heard them were said to go insane.

The word "mandrake" means, "the dragon which resembles man," and from what is seen of the plant, there is supposedly a female and male form, each looking so much like the two sexes of man that it is amazing. The way the roots sometimes wrapped around one another, it appears as if one plant were symbolic of a woman, and another, a man.

It is said that the Japanese grow a very powerful type of mandrake, which they call the ginseng, but it is different from that which was discussed as regular ginseng in the beginning of this chapter. It is said to differ from the mandrake in the West, as the plant has a stronger resemblance to the human form. This is possibly due to the different agricultural conditions in that country. The ancient magicians and priests believed that it was the root of creation. It was thought that the ancient Japanese sorcerers actually created life by manipulating the mandrake roots, then breathing life into them.

It is claimed by the old magicians that if anyone would pull up the mandrake root at midnight, in the light of the full moon, then clean it and write the name of his beloved upon it, that she would never leave him for another. Or if he would write whatever was his greatest desire in life, it would come true.

Of course, there were many other types of spells which the magicians used—for example, those that would bring money, improved health, mental stimulation, and fruitful crops. There are supposed to be no less than twenty-five different types of mandrake-based spells that the magician may utilize for his clientele. I seriously warn against anyone swallowing mandrake because of its poisonous properties. When mixed with other ingredients, the mandrake can be highly dangerous to the human body. The only way that it should ever be taken is under the direction of the family physician.

Carob, or St. John's Bread, is the fruit of the carob tree. Finely ground, it takes the place of cocoa, chocolate, and to some extent, sugar. It contains a sufficient amount of vitamins and minerals to qualify as one of the worthwhile plants which can be considered here. Although a tree, it is more or less a leguminous type of product. It is actually an evergreen tree of the senna tribe of the pea family.

It is a native of the eastern Mediterranean area. It grows to about fifty feet in height and has numerous branches, forming a rounded head with shining dark leaves, which have two or three pairs of leaflets. Its flowers are in small red clusters with numerous brown hornlike flat pods, which are from six to twelve inches long, one to one and one-half inches broad, and a quarter of an inch thick. The flowers contain many hard, small, dark brown seeds, which are imbedded in a sweet, mealy, edible pulp.

The pod and seeds removed from the mealy pulp are dried and ground up into a powder, which is used as a beverage instead of chocolate. It is also used in baking and candy making. Many who are allergic to chocolate, cocoa, and milk, use carob instead.

These pods are dark brown in color, rich in natural sugar and protein. They are important for food and forage. Mohammed's armies on the march sometimes lived on Kharub, or what is known as carob. The ancient Romans, Spaniards, and British all knew the carob tree and lived on its pods when other food was scarce. John the Baptist ate the carob pod in the wilderness, so it is stated, giving it the appellation, St. John's Bread.

Carob is used for animal feed and in the Latin American countries for an oil extracted for medical purposes. The wood is used for staining, and the roots contain medicinal properties. The grown tree can yield up to one thousand pounds of pods in a season.

It is exceedingly productive and there are orchards of carob trees in the warm climate states of America such as California, Florida, and Texas.

Medicinally, carob is a mild laxative and demulcent. Some singers use the pod husks in the belief that it clears their voice and helps their throat. Gum is extracted from the seeds and used in various industries such as textile, pharmaceutical, food, leather, rubber, and cosmetics. Carob gum is imported from several European countries.

Carob should replace the starchy sweets that we have learned to crave in this civilization. The refined sugar, which goes into so many of the sweets in our national food diet, is not at all good for body health.

Carob contains many vitamins and minerals. The body must take its good health out of everything which is given it. Unless every bite contains vitamins and minerals, it is harmful to burden the body with it.

Thiamine is that important B vitamin so necessary for proper digestion of carbohydrates and so essential for the good health of the nerves which, of course, makes for good morale. It also contains a good amount of Niacin, another B vitamin which is responsible for the health of the digestive tract. Another B vitamin product in carob is Riboflavin, which is needed for the health of the skin and eyes.

Carob also contains Vitamin A, the fat soluble vitamin, which protects the eyes from night blindness and infections, as well as calcium, phosphorus, iron, and magnesium. It is not necessary that carob be on the daily diet, but it is a staple and should be used in place of candy, which is needed to satisfy the desire for sweets in a child.

Of course, carob is not the full answer to the needs of the bodily intake of Vitamin B. We get more of this vitamin in meat, fish, and poultry, according to most authorities. Animal protein is a complete protein, which contains more essential amino acids than vegetable protein.

Meat is a high quality protein, rich in iron and the B vitamins, especially Riboflavin and Niacin. In the milling of grains, many of the B vitamins are lost. The use of meats in the diet provides these essential vitamins that are nonexistent in the devitalized processed food so prevalent today.

Americans are a meat eating people. In fact, most of the Occidentals are, and if they were not, they would be in bad health because of the excessive use of processed starches and sugars in the national diets.

Golden Seal is one of the old types of herbs used by the natives and ancients in many countries throughout the world. However, we mainly find it among the Indian tribes of North America, who once relied on it almost entirely for many of their medical needs. Not having the science of medicine as we do today, the North American primitives had to depend wholly upon the plant and herb kingdom for their medicinal needs. This was natural, and it has brought much of their findings into our research laboratories today so that we might understand just what the Indians had that helped them to keep their health under such primitive conditions.

The golden seal was one of their favorite herbs. It is a small perennial plant with a thick, fleshy yellow rhizome. It produces a solitary rose-colored or whitish flower. The fruit, which is produced only one time yearly, looks much like a raspberry, but it is not edible.

The golden seal grows in moist, rich woodlands in various parts of the United States, but it is far more abundant in the northeastern sections of the country. The natives of early New England settlements soon learned to use the golden seal herb and to make use of it for medicinal purposes. The name golden seal was given to this plant because of the seal-like scars on the golden yellow roots.

In the mid-south, the Cherokee tribe made great use of this marvelous little herb. The people used it as a remedy for sore mouths, inflamed eyes, and as a bitter tonic in stomach and liver disorders. They also employed its use externally for diseases of the skin, and it became very popular among the early settlers in the eastern part of the mid-south area. The fresh root is quite juicy, and it was used by the Indians as a dye for their garments and as a stain for faces during rituals and ceremonies.

Sometimes the golden seal is called yellow root, tumeric root, or Indian dye. It is native to Canada and the Eastern United States. It belongs to the buttercup family and resembles the raspberry. The Indians of North America used the plant originally as a dye and a sort of cosmetic. The tea brewed from the roots of the plant contains several valuable alkaloids of which hydrastis is the most important. Hydrastine is a bitter crystalline, nonpoisonous alkaloid found in the rootstock of the golden seal and used as a tonic. Its action is tonic, laxative, and purgative. It is a valuable remedy in digestive conditions, and it has a corrective local effect on the mucous membranes, especially in the inflammation of the colon and rectum.

The root of the golden seal, which is known scientifically as the *Hydrastis canadensis,* is a bright yellow color and is crooked and wrinkled. In the center of two rough leaves appears the flower, which is displaced by the large seeded berry. The root is used in the treatment of leucorrhea, inflammation of the bladder, and as a tonic to refresh and invigorate the muscular system of the body. It has a tone-up medicinal purpose.

During the early part of the nineteenth century, medical authorities began to experiment with the golden seal root because of reports they had from older generations who had made use of it. Accounts of the benefits of golden seal had been handed down from generation to generation, mostly by word of mouth from the Indian remedies. The Indians used it for strong tea for indigestion, low fevers, and for cases of general weakness. It was also used as a wash for inflammation of the eyes. Hydrastis, the product of the golden seal root, was given a careful review of its properties, uses, and preparations by the medical laboratories. As a result, it was declared an official drug in the pharmacopoeia of this country in 1860, and a great demand was created through its new uses.

In these modern times golden seal has become quite useful to the botanic industry in modern preparations. It is used in preparations for the eyes, such as eye drops and eye washes, as hydrastis is one of the chief ingredients in such medicines. It is also used in morning sickness, sore mouth and eyes, eczema, indigestion, and catarrh. Some medical authorities use it in their practices, so it is said, as a stimulating tonic in cases of indigestion and gastric debility, and for the nervous system.

This all indicates that diagnosis by computer and electronic apparatus today may not get to the right source of trouble in the human body and mind. Psychosomatic problems, which include depression, irritability, anxiety, fears, difficulties in concentration and the memory span, uncontrollable weeping, insomnia, fatigue, inability to make decisions, sensitivity to slight noises, and ferocious temper tantrums complicated by nightmares, shortness of breath, dizziness, blurred vision, and thoughts of suicide, can be due to a lack of a proper diet.

There is always a reason for what is happening to the body, and no one should expect a cure, healing, or a miracle to take place in his health after twenty-five years of bad nutrition. He created his own problem and he must bear the responsibility for it.

I will go back again to the problem of fasting,

which many of those who are of a religious bend of mind do not fully understand. Those who undertake a prolonged fast may lose a few teeth, peace of mind, and the ability to resist infection. These conditions are created when, and if, the individual who is going on such a fast has not prepared himself with plenty of Vitamin B6.

Those who fast may find themselves unable to enjoy their new proportion of religious visions and broadening of their outlook on life, because they have become too tense, irritable, and unable to sleep. They could also find themselves suffering oily skin, dandruff, and acne. These are the manifestations of a deficiency of Vitamin B6. This particular vitamin is necessary to the health of the skin and gums, the utilization of fats, the building of the blood, and the action of the muscles.

These are common symptoms found in studying the records of those religious figures who did so much fasting in order to gain some moving experiences of God. It has also been demonstrated by health authorities that a deficiency of Vitamin B6 does develop during prolonged fasts and specific manifestations may result.

It is not exactly that fasting alone will cause a deficiency of Vitamin B6, but a poor diet can bring about nervousness, insomnia, general weakness, and sometimes difficulty in walking. Even in the midst of plenty, where poor nutrition is not necessary, the same tendencies in the human mind and body are found. As much as eighty percent of the essential amino acid tryptophan is destroyed when Vitamin B6 is not properly supplied.

The individual should be certain about his health before attempting a prolonged period of fasting. Only if one is in fairly good health, can he have the necessary religious experiences. One should balance his nutritional life with other aspects of daily living.

The old religionists who were able to fast knew

quite a bit about their personal intake of food and what gave them particular problems, and what did not. They could sometimes go without food for days.

Today, although food is bountiful and there are relatively few people starving in the Western World, people may not be as aware of their nutritional problems and therefore have more difficulty in emulating the ancient religionists.

The golden rod is almost a twin to the golden seal plant. It is a plant which lends its color to the beauty of the countryside in the autumn of the year. The flowers are golden yellow—all turned in the same direction on the stalks. Golden rod is a valuable kidney and bladder remedy, the flowers and tops being used. It is also used as an antiseptic.

This plant is often called Aaron's Rod, Woundwort, Goldruth, Farewell Summer, to name a few. It has long been famous for healing wounds when used externally and, as an infusion, when taken internally. It has diuretic properties, and it has an excellent and time-honored reputation for dissolving kidney stones and ulcer pains.

The ancients used it for many of the above purposes, while in the modern age it has become an astringent. It is sometimes used, so it is said, for ulcers, and sometimes, as a spray in diphtheria.

The golden rod belongs to the thistle family. It grows in a great variety of places like woods, meadows, hills, and rocky ground. Golden rod was for a long time believed to be a cause of hayfever but experiments with its pollen have proven this is wrong.

Golden rod is a perennial herb with several species, many of them native to North America, but it originally was discovered in the ancient days in the Middle East. Traditionally it sprouted from Aaron's rod when he threw his staff upon the ground before the Pharaoh to demonstrate his magic. Golden rod has anise-scented leaves which are used to make an herb tea.

All these herbs seem to have played a definite part in the lives of the ancient mystics. Furthermore, they have had something to do with the evolution of man in the course of history. Every plant and herb which has added something to the assistance of man's health problems by curing him of some ailment, disease, or sickness, is considered a part of the growth of the human race.

The mystics have also played their part on the stage of mankind by their acute knowledge of plants and herbs, which not only helped with the nutritional value of diets for man, but also has assisted in his general health, keeping him well and fit to make his cities and country a better place to live.

Chapter Eight

# THE STRANGE
# AND CURIOUS HERBS
# THAT BRING HEALTH

Some readers may have wondered what the philosophy and doctrine of ECKANKAR, the ancient Science of Soul Travel, has to do with herbs, plants, and general health-giving foods.

The spiritual philosophy of ECKANKAR contends that the body should have good health in order to have a better life while here on earth. Pain is never pleasant, regardless of whatever age one is or under what circumstances he may suffer. Should a person be willing to suffer pain for the sake of his religious doctrine, well and good, but few can live in this world and still strive for spiritual understanding in ill health.

This book does not propose to replace the services of anyone's family physician. One should always consult him for any condition which requires his services. But the individual should take the responsibility of trying to keep himself in good health. He must learn something about nutrition and what his body chemistry can handle in the intake of general foods, herbs, and fruits.

The health and life-giving herbs, plants, flowers, and fruits have something to do with one aspect of ECK, and that is in the general area of health and healing.

ECKANKAR has thirty-two facets, among which two are of interest here. First, is the eighteenth facet, known as the banishing of pain and pleasure. This is part of the health and healing program which is under discussion in this book. Second, is spiritual healing, which is the twenty-seventh facet. I will touch upon spiritual healing here and there throughout the rest of the book.

We find that the ECK Herb Book is only one in the whole line of the spiritual works of ECKANKAR. Each of the thirty-two facets, discussed somewhat in the ECK-Satsang Discourses, First Series, will be covered sooner or later in the books which will be published on the overall subject of ECKANKAR.

In taking up the study of those strange and curious plants and herbs which give health to the mind and body of the individual, we are struck by the fact that so many of them seem to have been neglected by modern research, yet the generations of the past appeared to have gained from the use of them for general health.

The first we shall consider is the Eglantine, commonly known as Dog-Rose, or Sweet Briar. It is a part of the rose family known to science as *Rosa eglanteria.* It is a dense shrub often six feet tall and its stem bears hooked prickles. The upper side of the leaf is dark green, the underside is much lighter in color. The leaves have a pleasant aromatic odor. The flowers which blossom as inflorescences are bright pink and sweet scented. The fruit is orange-red or scarlet.

The eglantine is native to Europe, especially the central European countries. It has been widely cultivated in the United States for herbal uses.

The rosebuds ripen into a fruit called hip. The seeds are taken from the hips, dried, and a tea is made from them. The hip tea is good for purifying the kidneys and bladder. Those who have kidney stones should take a cup of this tea each day to resolve these irritants in the kidneys and bladder.

Cloves are the dried flower buds of the clove tree. Sometimes called spice clove, it is a part of the family known as myrtaceae. The clove comes from a tree which grows from fifteen to thirty feet high. It is an evergreen with a trunk measuring four to six feet with branches rising to form a pyramid. Its form is much like that of a bay laurel. The wood is hard and tough so that quite small branches will bear the weight of a man. The bark is somewhat smooth and bare. The stalk leaves resemble a laurel leaf, but are pointed and narrow. When young, they are a brownish red, becoming dark green and glossy on the top side, with an underside of yellowish green coloring.

The flowers are small, but bloom in great profusion in cymes. The leaves, flowers, and bark have an aromatic odor. The ripe fruit resembles an olive in shape, but is smaller in size. It is dark red in color, and sometimes appears commercially in a dried state under the name of mother cloves.

The flower buds are the principal products of the tree. They are gathered and are dried by exposure to the smoke of wood fires or to the sun rays. When first gathered they are reddish, but they change to a deeper brown color. Clove is native of the Spice Islands, but is now cultivated in Sumatra, the East and West Indies, Brazil and Guinea.

The oil obtained from the clove is sold by pharmacies, as well as being used for the base of many different patent medicines. From four to six drops of oil of cloves on a piece of sugar taken once or twice a day is a good remedy for stomach gases. Clove is also used for toothache, and, of course, as an herb for cooking and seasoning.

The properties of cloves depend chiefly on an essential oil known as the oil of cloves, which forms one-fifth of the whole weight and is used for flavoring. In addition, oil of cloves is sometimes used as an admixture of purgatives to prevent griping. In dentistry, it is used as an anesthetic and because of its mild antiseptic properties and pleasant taste, to flavor dentifrices. Being one of the least expensive essential oils, clove is also used in industrial perfumery, for example, in the scenting of soaps.

The elder, or black elder and common elder, as it is sometimes called, is a treelike shrub which grows from six to ten feet high.

It yields an herb that is used quite commonly by many who are living in the less civilized areas of the central European countries. The farm people and many who live in the country have used it for generations.

The bark of the trunk is light brown or gray, and rough. The branches are smooth with distinct wart-like bumps. The yellowish hard wood has a whitish pith. The stalks and flowers are herb-like in nature. The leaves consist of two and three pairs of leaflets, long and tapering at the base, long-pointed at the extremity, serrate dark green and hairless. The flowers are white or pale yellow and wheel-shaped. The berries grow to the size of peas, or smaller, and are dark violet or reddish and juicy.

The elder is a good spring tonic, according to an old German herbal formula which calls for the fine cutting of six to eight leaves to be simmered for ten minutes in a cup of water. A cup of this herbal water should be drunk before and after breakfast. It can be used at any time of the year and prepared from dried leaves if necessary.

The same German source says that a tea can be made from the flowers of the elder shrub which will produce a good remedy for dropsy.

A tablespoon of the elder berries boiled in sugar or honey and stirred into a glass of water will make a refreshing drink, clearing the stomach of gases and undigested foods, acting as a stimulant to the kidneys for diuretic purposes.

Another old German herbal formula called for boiling the dried berries to a pulp, simmering them into a tea or eating them dry for a beneficial effect in case of severe diarrhea.

One should remember that this is an old German formula for health, and he should obtain the advice of someone who knows the benefits of the elder, instead of depending upon remedies handed down through generations.

The butter bur is an herb which is a native of the Mid-European area. The flower stalk is about six to eighteen inches in height and as thick as a man's finger. It is covered with gray hair with a large triangular leaf that is pear-shaped at the base, smooth on the upper surface, and woolly gray beneath.

The flower is closely packed and oval. Its color is a purplish gray, and it is tubular in nature. Its tea is used in clearing the chest and lungs of phlegm. It is also used for treating coughs and tightness of the throat and chest. It is supposed to help reduce fever in consumption by putting wet leaves on the chest. Also, it is used to cool and relieve the pain of open sores, sore feet, and muscular fatigue. The leaves may be powdered and taken with food three times daily to help build the body.

Saint John's wort is a plant which belongs to the herb and shrub family called *Hypericaceae*. It is a native of the subtropical and temperate regions throughout the world. Some species are widely cultivated in gardens, and St. John's wort also grows wild on dry heaths, plains, roadsides, ridges, and in forest clearings.

It was named after the Apostle John during the Middle Ages by monks who developed gardens and were skilled in the medicinal use of herbs. The wort blossoms on St. John's Day and was believed to possess magical properties, such as protecting one against thunder and evil spirits.

Various healing properties have been attributed to the different species of the plant, generally as astringent, diuretic, and expectorant.

The flowers are infused in olive oil and applied to wounds and bruises. Both the flowers and leaves are used for a tea to help liver complaints. In one old herbal remedy, it is said that the older generations used it for pains in the head arising from congestion or catarrh.

It is a shrub which grows about two feet high, the stems springing from one root with auxiliary branches. The scrubby Saint John's wort is a native of the United States and bears an attractive yellow flower cluster. It is a popular garden flower used mainly for ornamental purposes.

The common Saint John's wort is the most abundant of the wild species and is known as a weed throughout the United States, as well as the rest of the world. The petals of its flowers are twice as long as the sepals and are golden yellow, dotted with black along the edges. The name, "Aaron's Beard" is also given to the Saint John's wort.

The Shepherd's purse is a small shrub which was used as a medical remedy in the older European generations, and still is today among many who live in the rural areas.

It is a plant which grows about one foot high. The stem is straight, and its root leaves are partly oblong and toothed. They are roughly serrated. The upper leaves are arrow-shaped and half embrace the stem with toothed margins. Its flowers are short, white, four petaled, and small. The fruit is long-stalked and the seeds triangular. It is easily recognized.

It is found throughout the world in fields, gardens, near homes, and on roadsides. It is especially abundant in the European countries.

It flowers throughout most of the year, especially in countries where the winters are mild. Its leaves, flowers, and husks are all used in herbal remedies. By simmering the leaves in wine or by reducing them into a powder and mixing them with wine, the herb may be drunk whenever needed.

Shepherd's purse is also a powerful diuretic and was used as a remedy for intermittent fever with enlargement of the spleen or liver, and for complaints of the stomach. This remedy was made up of a half handful of flowers and seed pods boiled in three cups of water. A cupful of this was drunk when needed.

The powder was also used for fresh wounds. It was supposed to have a powerful healing effect. The plant also was beaten into a mortar with vinegar to cool swellings of various kinds on the body.

The German valerian root is the proper herb to soothe and quiet the nerves when the nervous system is in a highly irritated condition, in high blood pressure and similar conditions.

The valerian is known by several other names—the great wild valerian, the German valerian, the all-heal herb, amantilla, setwall, the English valerian. It is a native of Europe and Northern Asia. It is found in woodlands, river banks, hedges, mostly in damp spots, but occasionally, in dry spots and barren slopes. It flowers in June and July, depending mainly upon the climate where it grows. Usually, it flowers best in July in the Northern Asiatic countries and earlier in European climates.

The valerian is noted for its roots, which give the herbal qualities for remedies. This root consists of numerous pointed, brown, closely packed rootlets, white in its interior, with a peculiar, fetid odor. The stem grows about three feet high, upright, round, and is hollow with leaves in pairs. The leaves are pointed, narrow, and toothed. The flowers form a many-colored corymb and the fruit buds are adnate. The flowers are tubular with five blunt parts and the color is flesh white.

The root alone is used and is generally dug in the spring, before the plant has begun its growth. It is cut and dried, then stored or made into powder. It must be kept airtight. It is useful in all sorts of nervous complaints, whether they consist of cramps, pains, headaches, or stomach gases.

Its medicinal action and uses are anodyne, nervine, and antispasmodic. It may be used in all cases of nervous debility, so the herbal authorities state. It is also used in irritation of the nerves and in hysterical afflictions. It allays pain and promotes sleep. It is said to be a strong nervine without any narcotic effects, and valerian is used in various herbal, nervine, and anti-spasmodic compounds. It is said to be useful in epilepsy and convulsions. The valerian root is supposed to influence the circulation, slowing down the heartbeat, increasing its strength.

The Oregon grape root is an herb which is common to the western coast of the United States and the Rocky Mountains. Its common names are the Rocky Mountain grape, holly leaved barberry, California barberry, and trailing mahonia. It is one of the best among the herbs for purifying the blood and as a stimulant for the liver.

The Oregon grape root is an evergreen shrub which grows to a height of approximately ten feet. It bears large, glossy, pinnate flowers with spiny, dark green leaves. Its flowers are yellow with six sepals, six petals, six stamens, and a solitary pistil. The fruit is an attractive, bluish blackberry. The plant is the state flower of Oregon, and it is cultivated as a hedge shrub in the United States.

The part used is the rhizome, the underground root-like stem that sends up leafy roots from the upper surface and emits roots from the lower side. They are boiled in distilled water and taken orally for weak digestion, jaundice, blood impurities, and as a general tonic for the whole body system. It is said that the herbal remedy made from the root will restore health and increase strength and vitality to many who are suffering from a sluggish liver, weak stomach, indigestion, and sallow skin.

The buckthorn is a shrub found in the temperate and tropical regions of Europe, Asia, Africa, and the Americas. The cascara buckthorn of the Pacific Coast of the United States is a tree fifteen to twenty feet high, the bark of which yields cascara sagrada, a laxative.

The common buckthorn, a shrub native to England, has been naturalized in the United States and has round, blue-black berries about the size of a pea. From these berries a strong cathartic is made. A yellow dye is also part of its use, prepared from the bark. There are several different kinds of buckthorn, and several different uses are prepared for herbal remedies from either the berries or bark.

The name, buckthorn, comes from the spines on the branches of some species. The leaves are bright green and oval; the flowers small, axillary, white, yellowish or green, and clustered. These plants are sometimes cultivated in shrub borders.

The buckthorn is an alder shrub. It is sometimes called the black dogwood, frangula bark, black alder dogwood. The part we are interested in here is a native of Europe and Northern Asia. The medicinal action and uses are tonic, laxative, cathartic, and only the one- to two-year-old plant is used, as the young herb causes severe griping.

Buckthorn is used as a tonic to cleanse the blood and stimulate the stomach bowels. Other uses come from the berries, which are boiled in syrup and administered in small doses to serve as a strong purgative, according to an old Mid-European herbal formula. Otherwise, buckthorn can be given with honey to modify its taste, if so prescribed by a recognized herbal authority or the family physician.

The passion flower is a native of the West Indies and the southern part of the United States. It is what we call a mystical flower because it is traditionally associated with the crucifixion. It is a climber and is regarded as one of the most lovely plants used for covering trellises and arbors.

There are several species, some of which produce fruits that can be eaten for food or made into juices in their native climes. As a climber, it often reaches the top of the highest trees where it is sustained by tendrils that produce an abundance of beautiful white and purple flowers.

123

When the Spanish first found this flower growing wild in America, the priests called it the flower of passion, because it represented to them something they associated with the crucifixion. Shortly after they came into this country, the Spanish sent the species back to Rome where it was cultivated and introduced into other countries.

The passion flower has small seeds and digitate leaves. Its medical ingredient is an ancient one; it has herbal sedative, antispasmodic, and nervine uses. It is still used in various parts of the world today for these particular elements in herbal remedies. It also is considered a reliable remedy in treating nervous disorders, insomnia, and hysteria. Some say that the herb is particularly effective in alleviating cases of occupational strain and severe mental stress, anxiety, and pressures of modern living.

In the United States, many of the sleeping pills and nerve sedatives sold in drug stores without a prescription contain the passion flower as one of their main ingredients.

Shave grass is a plant whose natural habitat is Great Britain, Sweden, and Australia. It is found in fields, pastures, and is common throughout the country, growing in all sorts of soil.

It has several different names—horsetails, horsetail grass, pewterworst, Dutch rushes, paddock pipes, and bottle brush. Only the herbaceous part : the green, barren shoots and the tails are used for any remedies.

It is a plant which grows about a foot in height, with its branches wiry and stiff, numerous and easy to pick off. These branches resemble the stiff hair of a horse's tail. There are several different species, but the quality of the branches is the same. Although some branches are arched and droopy, others have stiff, spreading branches which are somewhat bent.

The medicinal action and uses are diuretic and astringent, beneficial in dropsy and kidney afflictions generally. A dram of the dried, powdered herb, taken three or four times a day, has also proved to be effective in halting the spitting of blood, so say certain herbalists. Shave grass is said to be one of the best of the herbs for the treatment of cystic ulcerations and ulcers of the urinary passages and hemorrhages.

Shave grass is also good as an emmenagogue. It will stop bleeding and assist in healing. It is sometimes used in reducing the swelling of eyelids and parts of the face. It is said to be used by the natives in the rural areas of the countries where it grows as a remedy for nose bleed.

The tea made from the herb is said to clear the stomach of gases and to help in the digestion of food. In the Middle Ages, it was used to heal wounds from battle action.

Balm is a common name for a fragrant, perennial herb in the mint family. It is native to Europe and grows wild on wooded mountains and in hedges and vineyards. It has also long been cultivated in gardens.

The height of the plant is about one to three feet. It is bushy, erect, and has branches starting at the base. The leaves are grass green, rather heart-shaped, and the flowers, which blossom from July through September, are a light greenish white in color. The plant has a pleasant lemon-like scent.

The stems and leaves are still used occasionally in medicine as a gentle stimulant and tonic, and were once in great demand. The taste is somewhat astringent and the odor slightly aromatic.

The leaves are collected before the time of flowering, dried in the air, and are generally used in the form of tea, about one ounce to a half pint of water. The tea is drunk for body pains which arise from disturbances of the nervous system and for hysteria. Balm tea is also used for stomach cramps, digestive disturbances, and colic.

Balm was called melissa among the ancient Arabs

and was cultivated in gardens and hedges. The physicians often recommended it for affections of the heart; in other words, it was a love potion. Paracelsus, the famous herbal physician of the Middle Ages, claimed the drinking of balm tea would bring about the complete rejuvenation of whoever used it. Because of this claim, balm was often steeped in wine and used as an ingredient in love potions and brews.

Balm is among many herbs which seem to have been a part of the mythology of man. Curious legends have sprung up around balm.

"The balm of Gilead" is mentioned in the *Bible* a number of times. This balm comes from a small tree native to Arabia. A resin substance is taken from the trees and sold exclusively in Arabia and other Asiatic countries today. The buds of the tree are used as a medicinal remedy for ailments of the stomach, lungs, and kidneys. Sometimes it is used as an ointment for rheumatic and gouty pains.

The orange is another product to be taken up here as a use for herbal and health remedies. Of course, it is a fruit and considered so, but the orange may be used in several different ways as a source of vitamin products, as in the "C" vitamins and as a botanical for body health.

There were certain writers of the ancient period of history who flatly stated that the orange was really the mythical golden apple of Hesperides. Greek mythology is filled with stories about these golden apples. It is said that Zeus gave Hera an orange when they married, and as a result, its blossoms have become a bridal flower in many countries, including the United States.

However, it is now being proven out that the orange, as well as other citrus fruits, are important factors in the well-balanced diet. The orange possesses many valuable health and medicinal properties. The peeling of the orange was used during the 12th century as a tonic by the Chinese. A fermentation of its flowers was a remedy for the heart, and the juice mixed with water was remedial for certain fevers.

The orange is a native of South China and Indochina. We find that the ancient Chinese writings refer to oranges as early as 2200 B.C. Columbus carried orange seeds for planting in the New World. As early as the 16th century, orange plantings were made in Mexico and Central America. Oranges were planted in Florida in 1565, and in Southern California in 1769.

Lemons, too, are considered very important in the all-around diet of man. The lemon has a somewhat broader use than the orange in the medicinal field. It is a native of the tropical regions of India and Burma, where it has grown wild since prehistoric times. It spread from Persia to Egypt and Palestine about the year 1000, and it finally was introduced into Spain by the Arabs in the 12th century. Columbus brought the seeds to the West Indies from the Canary Islands in 1493, on his second trip to the New World. Since then it has spread to almost every tropical country in the world.

Lemons have been used in a variety of ailments, such as sore throat, colds, rheumatism, headaches, heartburn, upset stomach, hiccoughs, chapped lips, chilblains, and insect bites. The lemon was once used as a supplement to the diet of sea-faring crews to ward off scurvy and to add to the diet of undernourished people. At the present time, most of its medicinal use is for the pure extract, Vitamin C, known as ascorbic acid, and bioflavonoids.

Other citrus fruits used for the health of the body are the grapefruit, lime, tangerine, and the pitanga of Brazil. The latter is a good source of calcium, phosphorus, and iron. Brazil has several other health fruits which are the pinguin, grumichama, jagua, and pitomba. All have good Vitamin C content as well as iron, riboflavin, calcium, and enzymes that are useful to the body. They also have many other commercial uses.

Vervain, sometimes called verbena, is a plant which has its native origin in the United States, England, and some European countries. It is found along roadsides and in dry grassy fields. Other names for it are Wild Hyssop, Simpler's Joy, Herb of Grace, and Fit Plant.

It has been, since the beginning of time, a symbol of enchantment. It is said that the ancient magicians and priests used this mystic herb in their divinations. Vervain was dedicated to Venus, the Goddess of Love, in practically every ritual. Even today it is still regarded as a plant which possesses power as a love philtre.

It was a custom in the early days to steep the whole plant in water, which was then used for cleaning the house in order to keep away evil spirits. Another belief was that by wearing a few leaves on the person, the vervain might protect one from harm.

Vervain is an herb common in most countries with temperate climates. It is not only a nervine, but also a tonic, expectorant, anti-spasmodic, a vermicide, astringent, diaphoretic, and a diuretic. It will also correct, so it is stated, shortness of breath and wheezing, circulatory weakness. Vervain is said to aid convalescence following illness and to give help to liver and spleen ailments.

One of the better nervines is the Boneset. Its natural habitat is North America, growing in damp, swampy places, meadows, and on banks of small streams. It has long been recognized as a tea with a somewhat bitter flavor. Boneset was used by the settlers, who in the early days of this country had to live in adverse conditions in log cabins with earthen floors, where it was cold, damp, and miserable. They used Boneset tea as a nightcap to warm themselves, as well as a stimulant for their nerves.

Nervines, of course, act upon the nervous system to temporarily relax nervous tension, or sometimes, to excite or stimulate the system to a higher degree.

The parts used in Boneset are the dried leaves and the flowering tops. Boneset has several common names, such as Thoroughwort, Teasel, Augue Weed, Feverwort, Indian Sage, Rheumatism Root, Sweat Plant, and Fit Plant. It is versatile and used almost daily in herb remedies for a varied number of ailments. It is not only one of nature's greatest remedies for colds and fevers but it is also known as a good nervine, tonic, and anti-spasmodic.

The American Indians used it mainly to break the influenza fever, for Boneset is said to take away both the ache and fever. Its therapeutic properties include, besides those named in the above paragraph, it being used as a stimulant, diaphoretic, anti-periodic, emetic, and aperient.

The common sage, sometimes called the Sage of Virtue and Garden Sage, is a small scrubby plant with branching stems, which often grow to the height of twelve to twenty-four inches. They bear numerous leaves and are four-sided. The entire plant is covered with a very short, gray down. The leaves are oblong, much wrinkled on the surface, deeply wrinkled on the underside, with a mid-rib and arch-shaped veins. The flowers are in numerous whorls on long spikes which terminate the branches. Sage is of a velvet blue color, a half-inch long, somewhat deeply crenate in the center.

The sage is found in wild, rocky, barren places in the Southern Alps, in the Austrian Littoral, in the Canton Ticino (a part of Southern Switzerland), and in Illyria. It grows wild in Germany, especially in the chalk districts where the plant has long been grown for domestic purposes.

Sage is cultivated in gardens all over the world. Its time for flowering is June and July. The leaves are usually gathered before the plant blooms, and then it is dried and powdered. The flower is useless for any medicinal purposes, according to the European herbalists. Sage is used for bathing and dressing of long-standing open sores, and when it is used as a tea, will remove any discharge from the gums and throat. If the tea is mixed with wine and water, it purifies the liver and kidneys. Powdered sage sprinkled on food produces the same effect as stated here.

The ancients used it for seasoning food, which we follow today in herb cooking. It is an astringent, stimulant, and nervine. It is recommended for liver complaints. A mixture of honey and sage was a remedy used for consumption in the old days. Sage is recommended by herbalists for rheumatism. Laced with lemon and honey and boiled in water, sage is said to have the power to ward off colds. It is easily grown in a garden from seed or transplanted roots. It is a perennial herb.

The fenugreek is a plant found in countries throughout southern Europe. It is cultivated in the central part of that continent and has become quite wild in fields, wooded slopes, and even among planted crops. The time for its flowering is in June and July.

Its medicinal purposes are for inflamed throats, to reduce swellings and inflammation in wounds, and to prevent blood poisoning. It is used as a tea for reducing fevers.

Fenugreek is a plant which grows from six to eighteen inches high, and the leaves are triplicate, obovate leaflets. The flowers are single, double or triple, and its seed pod cylindrical. The seeds are ground and are used as an ingredient of curry powder, and for flavoring cattle food. They contain an alkaloid, trigoneloline, and have been used medically. Fenugreek is grown for fodder in India, as it was in ancient Greece.

The chicory, or wild succory, is a plant which grows in Europe and Asia. It is now also cultivated in the United States. It flourishes in uncultivated places, by roadsides, on dry plains, and in dry ditches. It is a perennial herb.

Roasted and pulverized chicory roots are used in adulterating coffee, or as a substitute for it. Tea prepared from the chicory roots has a purifying effect on the stomach, liver, spleen, and kidneys. Poultices of the whole plant may be applied to the parts affected where there is an inflammation of the body. Alcohol in which the chicory root has been steeped is good as a rubbing lotion to remove weakness of the limbs.

It is also said to be effective in jaundice, liver enlargement, gout, and rheumatic complaints when made as a decoction of one ounce to one pint of boiling water. It can be used as an appetizer and as a delicious salad or a vegetable, even during mid-winter.

## Chapter Nine

## HERBS AND THE WHEEL
## OF ECK-VIDYA

Anyone who is a student of herbology and nutrition knows that in order to maintain or re-establish the normal equilibrium of the body, certain inorganic minerals must be present in proper proportions. A deficiency of any of the essential minerals in the body may result in functional disorders, including nervous exhaustion, with symptoms of mental and physical depression, anxiety, nervous dread, irritability, despondency and brain fatigue, especially intensified by overwork or worry.

This brings us to the *Bhavachakra,* the Wheel of Life, or that which those in ECKANKAR call the Cycle of the ECK-Vidya. The ECK-Vidya is a method of divination based upon the very ancient understanding of the Samsara. This is the Wheel of Life which is used by the Tibetans to inform the mind of man of the very nature of existence.

Within the ECK philosophy it is found that one who has knowledge of this Wheel of Life is indeed fortunate. He knows there are twelve sections (representing the twelve months of the Western calendar) and that it takes twelve years to complete one cycle. This means that it takes one hundred and forty-four years to complete a full cycle of a single existence. This should actually be the longevity of every man's life on earth, but it is not, because of a lack of a proper balance of minerals in the body. As a result, few people live beyond the age of seventy-five.

Most ECK Masters will generally live to this age

and beyond, according to the type of work they have to do while living here in their earthly bodies. Each ECK Master during his time here has constantly pointed out that each man is unique and that a set rule cannot apply to each individual spiritually or physically.

Rebazar Tarzs, the great ECK Master, said, "Man has lived too long with the idea that there must be a best way for him to collectively do everything. He must change his traditional thinking in terms of normal and average, so as to better understand the individual patterns in all aspects of his life. He must come to know himself."

The world is now a melting pot. Every country harbors a mixture of races. Each group has its own acquired habits, among which are nutritional habits. Orientals traditionally eat little meat, mostly because of its scarcity. But they get their protein from fish and soybeans. The Eskimos are largely meat eaters, because plant life in their world is scarce. Those living in the equatorial countries subsist primarily on plants and fruits.

We find that the size of portions, frequency of meals, and content of the meal varies considerably among man. Patterns are due to climate, habit, type of life, work, temperament, and physical body type. One's own heredity from his immediate family, his early childhood conditioning and his emotional life pattern play an important part in the selection of foods.

The hunger for starches, sugar, and alcohol is a perverted appetite, according to Fubbi Quantz, who is the Abbot of the Katsupari Ashram in Northern Tibet. An appeal only to the taste buds is certainly an incorrect approach to one of the most vital issues of physical and spiritual health. Men usually overeat carbohydrates, for they have no self-discipline concerning the appetite.

The Wheel of the ECK-Vidya has twelve spokes,

which are the original sections of time which made up the calendar of all nations that have existed on earth. In ancient times there were thirty days in each month. This segmentation made thirteen months. In the course of time, however, the present calendar was worked out. In those ancient days the months were named for rare jewels.

By the use of measurement we can somewhat compare the months of the present calendar with the ancient ECK calendar. They are as follows: January—the month of the emerald, called *Astik*, the days of wisdom; February—the month of the bloodstone, called *Uturat*, the days of love; March—the month of the jade, called *Garvata*, the days of joy; April—the month of the opal, called *Ebkia*, the days of hope; May—the month of the sapphire, called *Ralot*, the days of truth; June—the month of the moonstone, called *Sahak*, the days of music; July—the month of the ruby, called *Kamitoc*, the days of freedom; August—the month of the diamond, called *Mokshove*, the days of light; September—the month of the agate, called *Dzyani*, the days of friendship; October—the month of the jasper, called *Parinama*, the days of beauty; November—the month of the pearl, called *Hortar*, the days of wealth; and December—the month of the onyx, called *Niyamg*, the days of charity.

According to ancient knowledge handed down by the ECK adepts, here is what one should include in his daily diet during the varied months of the old calendar. This is based upon the vibrations of the physical and mental selves during these particular periods.

Health comes, of course, with the adjustment of the vibratory rates within one's self. This is what the ECK Masters do for anyone who approaches them for healing. The foods given here, which one should include in his diet for these varied months, should help in a similar way.

135

In *Astik*, the month of the emerald, one should have as much sage, valerian, lettuce, beans, nuts, and dried fruits included in his diet as possible.

In *Uturat*, the month of the bloodstone, one should have such foods as lettuce, sea food, green leafy vegetables, mushrooms, and mint in his diet.

In *Garvata*, the month of the jade, one should eat mainly watercress, onions, wheat germ, and chives. These will help balance inharmonies in the body.

In *Ebkia,* the month of the opal, one should include in his diet the following foods: apples, peppermint, almonds, grapefruit, figs, peaches, and spices.

In *Ralot*, the month of the sapphire, one should have in his daily meals caraway seed, cheese, sea foods, raisins, dates, peaches, apricots, and walnuts.

In *Sahak*, the month of the moonstone, one should have a certain limited amount of lean meats—mainly beef, chicken, turkey, and fish. Also included in the diet must be citrus fruits, tomatoes, raw cabbage, and sea foods which contain much iodine.

In *Kamitoc*, the month of the ruby, one should be very considerate of his diet by eating eggs, liver, saffron, cherries, oats, and fruits with pitted centers.

In *Mokshove,* month of the diamond, one should eat garlic, cheese, raw sugar, carrots, dried fruits, and lean meats. Pork should be excluded from the diet altogether.

In *Dzyani*, the month of the agate, one must include the following in his daily intake for better health: peaches, cherries, peas, and yellow vegetables. One should build up his energy and vitality as much as possible for the coming months of winter.

In *Parinama*, the month of the jasper, one should consume meat, eggs, fresh milk, dried fruits, and yellow vegetables. However, one must eat sparingly in order to give his stomach a rest from the months past.

In *Hortar*, the month of the pearl, one must eat as much as possible of the following foods: asparagus, figs, carob, sage, cauliflower, turnips, turkey, chicken, and wild game, if it can be had.

In *Niyamg*, the month of the onyx, one should consider in his diet fish, especially halibut and cod, whole grains, lean meats, baked potatoes, peas, corn, and beans.

One finds that in order to have perfect health in the world of matter, time, and space, where we live in the physical body and are subject to the laws of nature, one must learn to break agreements with his traditions, environment, and surroundings. One develops strength from the inner side of himself when he learns to make these shifts in himself.

The mineral chart, according to the old ECK calendar which corresponded with the months, is established as follows:

In *Astik* we have the corresponding minerals which are best to be emphasized—phosphorus, bromine, and magnesium.

In *Uturat* one should look to the following minerals in order to be healthier: iron, copper, and potassium.

In *Garvata* one must look to the minerals which will make him a better thinker and give him good health around the upper part of his face and skull. These are fluorine, iodine, and sulphur.

In *Ebkia* one should include in his daily nutritional intake, iodine, silicon, and fluorine.

In *Ralot* one should think of the following minerals for better living—cobalt, silicon, and copper.

In *Sahak* one should give more attention to potassium, sodium, and chlorine.

In *Kamitoc* one must be very considerate of the minerals calcium, iodine, and chlorine.

In *Mokshove* one should think carefully about adding to his daily diet foods which contain an abundance of sulphur, zinc, and trace minerals.

In *Dzyani* one must include in his diet the minerals sulphur, zinc, and cobalt.

In *Parinama* one must consume those foods which will have a greater amount of magnesium, zinc, and copper.

In *Hortar* one must look to phosphorus, calcium, and manganese for better health.

In *Niyamg* nutrition for better health should include such minerals as phosphorus, sodium and iron.

This is only a suggested chart, but it was used many centuries ago by the ancient peoples when ECK was a major faith and when many followed it openly. Many of the minerals have already been discussed and will be further studied in later chapters, along with other important data about them.

Good health should be our birthright, but few have ever been this fortunate. In order to have greater relationships between one another and to give up the strain and stress of life, we must again take up the ancient ways of the ECK teachings. If we can come together as a world community again, as in the ancient days before the antediluvian flood, the health of the individual will be more perfect.

The community life and ways the ancient ECK Masters planned for man to live are still possible today if man will follow the perfect system. The most distinctive characteristic of such a social organization, which includes a political and economic system, is a combination of autocratic rule and communal development. One-fourth of the agricultural crops and industrial products go to God to be placed in huge storeplaces for lean years; one-fourth go to the state; one-fourth go to the producers; and one-fourth go to the poor, aged, and infirm. Under such a system, poverty is rare and destitution is unknown. Society is organized as a collective one under a benevolent authority, who is usually the MAHANTA, the Living ECK Master, or one who is appointed by him. Food is stored in special depositories as a defense against depression or lean years. An obligatory labor system is the basis of production, and is self-serving. Social life is built around the family, not the individual. Clans are established in village communities. These communities have leaders who allot tasks, share rewards, and administer punishments.

The domains of religion, state, and community are merged in this social system. There are no profit systems and no exchange of currency; labor is provided by cooperation. Ownership of land is communal, but families have their own homes which are private property. It is the socialist and free enterprise systems merged into one working modus operandi.

The world's people must find a different system under which to live than the present ones which are governing the various nations. This is not a criticism of any particular government, but of the social conditions existing throughout the world today.

Americans are considered the best fed; and, therefore, the healthiest people in the world. But this is not necessarily true. Few people, even in this country, have a knowledge of good nutrition. Nutrition is the key to good health and longevity.

Two-thirds of the world's population is underfed and suffer from infectious diseases. What we have failed to see in our antiseptic civilization is that disease and sickness develop an immunity to our artificial defenses. They seem to thrive even more on our constant fight to get rid of them than they do in those areas where sanitary conditions are lax. A child who is raised in an environment without proper sanitary conditions will often develop a ruggedness which will give him an ingrained defense against disease and sickness. Whenever a person lives close to the soil and is able to get food from his garden, meat from the fields, and water from his well, he is getting more natural ingredients than those who live in cities.

As a nation, this country has an unusually large amount of sickness. It has been shown that at least nine hundred out of every thousand suffer from some defect and disorder. It is also said that one out of every four has cancer. The figures for those having heart trouble is supposedly sixteen million. The latter is the number one killer in this country, due to the stress and strain of our modern civilization. Some eight million are claimed to be arthritic victims. Diabetes patients run into a figure of about three million. Another three million are claimed to be mental patients.

One wonders if nature, in some way, outwits our scientific and medical researchers in order to keep down the population. There are just as many children who die at an early age today, according to insurance company statistics, as there were before the advent of modern medicines. All this makes one ponder what the answer is for good health, longevity, and happiness.

Few of us realize that it takes time to rebuild health, to keep ourselves disciplined in proper eating habits which will help take care of the body functions and structure.

We do not want to acquire a faddist attitude. Making food a fetish can also promote careless nutrition. Many believe they can have eternal youth by following certain dietary formulas, by the eating of particular foods, and by listening to those who promise nutritional cures for certain diseases. Hopefully, the intelligent person will readily identify those who are merely handing out propaganda and the scientific findings which soothe and lull millions into becoming complacent about their diets.

There has never been a large scale survey of Americans' diets which would lead anyone to the firm conclusion that we are well fed. Nor has there ever been a survey made of national health which would reveal that Americans are healthy people.

The practice of eating moderately of simple foods should be of vast importance to all. The habit of eating too much of even the best nutritional foods, or eating them in indigestible combinations with other foods, can be as bad as eating poor foods. It is true that we can live on about half of what we consume. Too many mothers will overfeed their children, mainly to satisfy their own natural desire to see them happier. Somehow or other, a child, in its native wisdom, manages to get enough to satisfy its vital needs. No child should be coaxed or urged to eat when not hungry. It is good to let him go without a meal once in a while if he does not appear to be hungry.

We find that the strict followers of religion, especially members of the Greek Orthodox Church in Southeast Europe, are known for their longevity. Their faith imposes dietary restrictions and frequent days of fasting. When the appetite is stimulated by large varieties of foods, we are usually tempted to eat far more than we should, because we wish to satisfy taste, rather than hunger.

Anyone can keep healthy on a small daily intake of food, provided the vitamins and minerals are sufficient. Any manual laborer or one who participates in sports can easily do well on a minimum of two meals daily, while the rest of us can make it on a single meal.

It is a well known fact that if one tries to study or to seek spiritual enlightenment excessively, he will have a decrease of progress in this field. It is also known that if one gives a machine an excess of fuel, it decreases its power quite as readily as if it lacked fuel. The human body reacts in the same manner. If we overload the body with foods, it will soon stop functioning and begin to decay before its time. It often takes a long time before we can discipline the appetite, but if we do, then our weight will return to normal and we can do our work more efficiently.

In the same manner of thought, no one should combine concentrated proteins with concentrated starches in the same meal. When eating protein foods such as meats, fish, poultry, eggs, or cheese, it is best to combine them with green vegetables like lettuce, watercress, turnip greens, and celery.

Since different types of food require different kinds of enzymes for digestive purposes, it is best to eat them separately. Some health authorities will refute this idea, saying that certain natural foods contain both protein and starch.

Do not eat more than one kind of protein during the same meal. For example, do not order an egg and cheese omelet, or if fish is served, do not have meat. It is against the rules of good health to have meat and milk during the same meal. We find that proteins of a different type will nullify, or work against one another. This creates digestive problems, and if done often, the stomach will reach the point where it cannot properly digest the intake of meats and other fleshes for bodily needs.

On the other hand, do not mix acid fruits with starches, as the acidity is bad for the enzymes upon which starch digestion depends. Such fruits as pineapple, citrus, tomatoes, or any very sour fruit, will destroy the ptyalin enzyme upon which starch digestion is dependent. The first of the starch digestion is nullified, and the breaking up of the starchy intake then falls upon the pancreatic juices. One should drink any acid juice such as orange, grapefruit, or pineapple, at least fifteen minutes or more before eating cereal. Those who obey this rule generally eat acid foods or subacid foods alone and do not bother with any additional food.

It is best never to take two concentrated starches at the same meal. One should never combine bread and potatoes, as this leads to the overeating of a food that is required in small amounts only. It has nothing to do with the enzyme compatibilities, but such combinations lead only to overeating.

One must always remember that there is a limit to the effective functioning of the enzymes, and if one will provide the right food at each meal, then digestive juices will function more efficiently.

If the body has its digestive functions impaired, the whole modus operandi will be out of regulation. The vital organs of the digestive tract, therefore, must be given deep thought and understanding or one will suffer the consequences. This means that we cannot eat according to our likes and dislikes. Taste should not enter into the selection of foods at a meal.

The first consideration is to know what to drink. If fruits and vegetables make up a large proportion of our diet, then we do not require extra liquid. One should not have water at mealtimes, regardless of whether or not it is a fruit and vegetable meal. The habit of drinking water at a meal should not be encouraged, for it has the tendency to dilute and flush vitamins and minerals from the body.

Chlorinated water or regular tap water is not good for the body health. Most tap water is no longer pure water but a complex chemical solution which contains a number of additives, mostly fluorides. Fluorine has been introduced into the public water system to reduce tooth decay in young children, but it has been found that over a period of years of drinking water which contains fluorine, damage to the kidneys, liver, and heart may result. We also find that chlorinated water uses up the Vitamin E in the body, causing a loss of iodine.

The use of natural spring water for body health, especially that which is bottled at the source, tends to increase vitality and maintain the vigor of whoever uses it.

While on this subject, it has been pointed out that many synthetic fruit drinks and carbonated beverages are among the worst toxoids available. Usually they consist of water colored with a coal tar dye, refined white sugar with an added synthetic flavor, phosphoric acid, and caffeine. In all, they represent few vitamins and natural minerals for the body's intake.

Only the freshly squeezed juices contribute to good health. When one drinks these fresh juices, it will be found that his desire for synthetic and carbonated drinks will cease. The canned and bottled drinks have little, if any, enzymes. Processed drinks that are sold as reconstituted fresh juices are pasteurized and have preservatives to keep them appearing fresh to the consumer.

One may use coffee substitutes, such as cereal or dandelion coffees, which are available in practically every health food store. Too much regular coffee, as most health experts know, will create a deficiency of Vitamin B, especially those elements of Vitamin B called inositol and biotin. Enough caffeine will cause nervousness in the heavy consumer of coffee.

There are dozens of herb teas known for their respective healing power, such as camomile tea for gall bladder troubles, mint tea for digestion, horehound tea for coughs and colds, and shave grass tea for the kidneys.

The trouble with regular tea is the bromine element, which is similar to caffeine in coffee. Bromine destroys the nerve cells and eventually interferes with the memory. Both tea and coffee lower the blood sugar. In those countries where tea is the main drink, people who are constant users of it will, over the centuries, become debilitated as a whole. Their natural energies start going down as a collective group of people. They become overwrought and highly emotional over very minute matters.

By omitting white sugar and starchy diets there could be an elimination of dental cavities in our growing children. It is said that the Eskimos of Alaska had perfect teeth until modern civilization arrived in the north country. Today most of the Eskimos have false teeth before the age of twenty-five. This is due to the white sugar and dietary products made of refined foods which reached them through the coming of the white man into their world.

One of the greatest health hazards is refined white sugar. The disturbance of the body's calcium-phosphorus balance is brought about by an overuse of white sugar. The relationship of calcium to phosphorus is important in maintaining the proper proportion of minerals in the body.

A better way to satisfy a sweet tooth without the use of products which contain refined, white sugar is a diet consisting of fruits, vegetables, whole grains, nuts, eggs, and milk. This provides the body with the equivalent of almost two cups of sugar daily. It also decreases the appetite for sweets. One particular point to make here is that sugar is not needed for energy, as we have been told by advertisers. Dried fruits contain about seventy-five percent carbohydrates, which are converted into sugar when digested. Anyone can nibble on dates, mission figs, and other dried fruits between meals in order to satisfy this type of hunger.

Any type of candies made from honey and carob are also useful as sweets. These can be found in most health food stores. Carob is often substituted for chocolate and sugar. It is made from carob meal which is ground from the pods of the honey locust trees found mainly in the Middle East and Asiatic countries.

Good raw sugar is hard to obtain, but one who is interested can find it as pure cane sugar. Often this comes from the fields of Hawaii and is packaged in boxes without the processing that is done for white sugar.

For good sources of natural sugars, well endowed with minerals and vitamins, one should try maple syrup and blackstrap molasses. Honey is another valuable, highly concentrated food, which gives vitality and general good health when eaten with meals. It may also be used as a base in products for between meal nibbling, especially for children.

Honey increases the hemoglobin count of the blood because of its content of copper, iron, and manganese. It is a quick way of getting energy, as it is largely predigested dextrose and does not have to go through the lengthy processes of body digestion.

Bananas are also a good source of energy and another way of satisfying the desire for sweets. When one eats a naturally ripened banana he gets calcium, phosphorus, iron, and Vitamins, A, B, and C. The average sized banana contains less than one hundred calories.

Millet is the best whole grain for anyone, whether it is taken as hot breakfast food or made into a bread. It is high in protein, minerals, and vitamins and does not have the fattening effect of wheat.

Peasants throughout the Orient often must subsist on very small portions of food during time of famine. Many times they have gone through these starvation periods on a diet consisting mainly of millet. In some cases such diets have cured stomach ulcers and improved the health of those who have used them.

Rice is not the universal food in Asia, except in the south. The northern areas grow millet as the staple food and have done so since recorded time. We will find that the population is stronger and more vigorous in the north than in the other areas where the populace lives entirely on rice as the staple food.

There are four foods which will help one maintain the standard needs of vitamins and minerals in the body. They are kelp, which furnishes practically every mineral needed by the body; citrus fruits, for Vitamin C content; Brewer's Yeast, which give Vitamin-B complex vitamins; and wheat germ oil, which contains Vitamin E. With the Vitamin-B complex and Vitamin E added to one's daily intake of food, he should have exceedingly good health.

## Chapter Ten

## THE SACRED HERB
## OF THE ECK MASTERS
## FOR LONGEVITY

For centuries, the principal food of the poor has been bread, and bread is still the chief ingredient of the diets of many poor people in remote areas of the world. One cannot live on carbohydrates, starches, and sugar without suffering from the effects of this type of eating.

It can be noted without having to resort to statistics that the death rate among the poorest of people is high compared to that of those who are able to furnish themselves with better nutrition. The Industrial Revolution brought with it the need for cheap, nonperishable foods for urban areas, where man had to collect in order to make a living in industry and where he was not in a position to raise his own food.

Because of this, the methods of processing foods arose. Unfortunately, processing removed many of the life giving ingredients, leaving nothing but starches. What was taken out went to feed animals, so that they would be in good health to serve as dairy animals or to be slaughtered and fed to the people of the cities.

The present young generation is not as bright and intelligent as we believe. The British have collected results of tests given English school children, aged eleven, since 1914. According to Sir Cyril Burt, in spite of the vast improvement made in social conditions during the last fifty years and the alleged improvements in educational methods, there have been no signs whatever that the average level of intelligence has been raised. Nor has there been any discernible leveling of the intelligence of the duller children, nor any indication that brighter children have grown in proportion.

Of course, there have been fads in better reading, spelling, and other facets of education. The advent of television has brought about a certain amount of learning, but this is not intelligence. Learning is the art of logical self-expression and the ability to draw conclusions from experiences.

We find that fifty to one hundred years ago parents were in a much better position to put food on the table which was fresh from the soil or unprocessed. This may be the reason why we have had such a leveling of intelligence. Vitamins, minerals, and other life-sustaining factors are withdrawn from processed foods and substitutes often replace them. As a result, the daily diet today has become fifty percent concentrated starch and sugar, practically all of which has been deprived of the elements needed to sustain life.

Poor health created by too much sugar and starch has caused many people to take drastic measures for healing. Often one can be the victim of advertising, tradition, or plain ignorance, because the general public has never been educated in good nutrition. We also have religious influences which regulate the diet of millions. Many people would starve rather than eat bacon and eggs for breakfast. Others would never touch meat from a cow.

Also, we have to consider the ethnic aspects of nutrition. Ethnic influences have created more problems for people than religious biases. We also have the faddists and cultists who are willing to listen to anyone who can make even a vague promise to rid one from defects and illnesses through nutrition.

Most people do not realize that the stress of hard

work can cause a depletion of such critical vitamins as C, B-1, and the readily utilizable fatty acids of the polyunsaturated types. There may also be critical shortages of magnesium, potassium and calcium. Most hard working people seem to have a major deficiency in fresh, natural, unheated oils of such grains as wheat germ oil. This could be, according to health authorities, because they tend to eat a heavy carbohydrate diet and neglect other foods, especially green, yellow and red vegetables and fresh fruits.

No longer do we eat food grown in the soil where we live that contains the minerals of which our bodies are made. Most of our ancestry was born and lived in the same community. The minerals in the soil and water become a part of the individual.

Our ancestors had longevity, and few of us do today because we are eating potatoes grown in Maine or Idaho, eggs from chickens raised in the deep South, meat that comes from the West, grain that is raised in the Midwest, and vegetables from California and Florida. So little food comes from the soil where we are living. Our longevity has taken a drop, and we are unable to find what is wrong with ourselves when we reach the end of our body's endurance because of a lack of minerals and vitamins.

Most Americans would die on the diet regimen of the Orientals, because their bodies have become used to a different diet. The city restaurants of Akita, Japan, serve what is considered the secret of a long and vigorous life. Akita is a city on the Japan Sea, near Hokkaido, and is noted for its main meal called *shottsuru ryori.*

The special dish in this meal is similar to *sukiyaki.* The difference is that chunks of carp fish are used instead of beef, and the liquid in which all is simmered is the elixir which is said to give long life and which is found only at Akita.

In other places the liquid used is the usual type made with a fish base. But in Akita the elixir of life is said to be that of an ancient recipe. It is made of hormones which have been buried underground for a considerable length of time so that they may ripen like wine. The restaurant owners put considerable stock in their recipe of the *shottsuru ryori* because the women remain younger and more beautiful than in other cities, and the men more youthful and vigorous. It seems that perhaps they have discovered something that the rest of the world knows little about.

The herb which is most important in the lives of people today, and one known to the ECK Masters for centuries, is the *Fo-Ti-Tieng*, or the Hydrocotyle Asiatica, a plant with extraordinary rejuvenating effects on the human brain cells and endocrine glands. Scientific and medical researchers says it contains an unknown vitamin.

Since this vitamin has not been fully researched, it has been given the name of Vitamin X. It is found only in the marshy, jungle areas of Ceylon, South China, and Southwest Asia. With Ginseng, which has already been discussed elsewhere in this book, Gotu-Kola, Panax schinseng, Sassafras, and Sarsaparilla, this ancient, but recently discovered plant has given man hope for longevity.

The acceptance of death at the ages between sixty-five and seventy is normal, although science says that demise at such an age could be premature due to undernourishment of the cells of the body. It is said that old age is due to the fact that the organs which make the cells of the body diminish and cannot function in the reproduction of cells that make up the body tissues.

Tissue cells are important if they have essential nutrition, for then they will promptly remove all wastes and poisons and function for any length of time, often beyond the normal span of the body's life. If this is true, then the answer lies in the fact that one should find the proper herbal preventative remedies. Our ancestors knew the beneficial properties of herbs and roots that grew in the woods and fields, which are gradually regaining their place in modern medicine.

*Fo-Ti-Tieng* is called the "Elixir of Life" or "Long Life Elixir." It is a low growing herb found only in certain parts of the jungles of the East. It is not a plant which would attract the attention of most people, yet it has become well known among Chinese and Eastern Hindu scholars as a food which contains a great life-sustaining property.

It is found in Asia and the East Indies. Its action is aromatic, corrective, diuretic, nutritive, as well as being used as a stimulant and a tonic. It has several uses as a remedy besides a defense against old age. It is used to combat fevers, piles, bowel complaints, and scrofulous conditions. It is said to strengthen and energize the brain.

A few leaves a day are taken, but it appears that they are chewed, rather than drunk in a tea. The plant grows only a few inches high and is a rather dull green color. The leaves are green and fan-shaped. The roots appear to be extremely long, perhaps twice the length of the plant stem above ground. Of course, at this length, the roots would be able to absorb the minerals of the soil in which it grows. This plant always grows in remote marshy areas.

The *Fo-Ti-Tieng* does possess the virtue of good health and longevity. It is not necessary to eliminate meat or flesh proteins, as so many do for the sake of gaining long life, but often the leaves may be ground up and put in with stews and soups. It is said to produce a general sense of good feeling, clear thinking, energy, and an improvement in appearance.

Many of the ECK Masters during the early days on this planet developed the *Fo-Ti-Tieng* for the purpose of helping people overcome many of their ailments and to create a good life without pain and unhappiness. However, in the past few centuries, the practice has died out because they have found that it brought about an interest more in the material side of life rather than the spiritual.

The ECK Masters have specific spiritual exercises which give them longevity. These extraordinary adepts of the East are actually God-Eaters, not in the symbolic sense that the Christians eat the body of Christ in the sacramental host and drink the Saviour's blood as wine, but the ECK Masters eat the cosmic energy which is the ECK, that spiritual power which flows out of God. They do this purposely for survival, the same as man eats material food to keep his body alive.

Until one learns to live outside the physical state of consciousness in the Soul body, he cannot hope to progress to such a spiritual life as the God-Eaters, the *Eshwar-Khanewale*. The God-Eaters live in a strange city called Agam Des, one of the spiritual cities of the world located near the tremendous peak of Tirich Mir in Central Asia, which rises to the height of 25,263 feet. It is the highest point in the Hindu Kush range of mountains which border Kashmir, Afghanistan, and Pakistan.

Agam Des means the inaccessible world, and it certainly is, for not only is its position hidden deeply in these remote wilds, but no one is allowed there unless by invitation from the ancient brotherhood of the God-Eaters. When one goes there it must be done by the *Nuri-Sarup*, the light body, escorted by the Living ECK Master.

When one first hears of this mysterious group of adepts and their incredible teachings, he finds it all very hard to believe. They are said to be in control of the secret forces of the cosmic life which gives human history its many changes and shapes in this world.

It was only after I had made contact with the great ECK Master, Rebazar Tarzs, that I became acquainted with the *Eshwar-Khanewale* in their secret city of Agam Des. Tarzs also brought to my attention the deeper knowledge of ECKANKAR, the Ancient Science of Soul Travel. The basic credo of the spiritual works of ECK is that man is a spiritual co-worker with God, that man has access to liberation and freedom in this lifetime, and that he always has, and always will, exist through eternity as Soul.

It is through supernatural energy that the God-Eaters can supervise the spiritual law. They have this ability because the supernatural energy is secondary to the knowledge of the spiritual law.

When one learns to live in the other worlds, he is then able to give up the foods of this earth world and live as the God-Eaters, who consume the ECK as their food. St. Catherine of Sienna was an eater of the cosmic spirit, as is Rebazar Tarzs, the great ECK Master who has lived here since 1452. Other great ECK Masters who are adepts in the art of survival through spirit are: Fubbi Quantz, head of the Katsupari Monastery in the Northern Tibetan Mountains, who is several centuries older than Rebazar Tarzs; Sudar Singh, my first ECK Master in India, who was one hundred and five years old at the time of his death; the old Chinese ECK Master, Suto T'sing, who lived for two hundred sixty-seven years in the same body; the well-known ECK Chinese Master, Lai Tsi, who is the head of the Temple of Golden Wisdom located in the etheric world, who lived on earth for a half dozen centuries. Heading up the order of the ECK Masters is Yaubl Sacabi, whose age is beyond human conception. He is the head of the city of Agam Des, and the present leading ECK Master of the Order of the Vairagi here in this world.

The ancients learned the extension of consciousness and moved into the higher states, proving that longevity is possible. The art of good health comes with the knowledge and ability of Soul-Travel. We find that Soul Travel can be used for self-healing and will take us into the world of good health and prosperity. But not many of us will become like the adepts of ECKANKAR, many of whose bodies last for centuries, because we have no purpose for living this long in this world.

These God-Eaters absorb the ECK, the cosmic energy, at a fantastic rate. By doing so they use their physical bodies to serve the planets, including the earth world, and the inner planes which are the astral, causal, mental, etheric (subconscious), the Atma (Soul), and the planes of pure spirit. They serve, not merely because the spiritual law demands service to all beings, but also in self-interest, for should the atmosphere become too loaded with radiation they will move to another planet or higher universe. They work best from the earth planet, because the flow of cosmic particles is greater here than in the other parts of this physical universe.

The reason we wear this physical body for a few score years is due to our Karmic debt. Unless we dispose of this Karmic debt we must go from one lifetime to another in various incarnations. The only way that one can become free of this Karmic debt in a relatively short time is by finding the Living ECK Master, and eventually becoming initiated by him. Such initiation takes one off the Wheel of the Eighty-Four, which is that treadmill of rebirth and death in this physical universe.

There is another method of rejuvenating body health known as the *Ayur Vedha*, a system of renewing the health and youth of the physical body. Sometimes it is known as the *Kaya Kalp*, which means life-time. In other words, it offers a second life. It is part of a system of spiritual practices which is somewhat known in India, but is a part of the rejuvenation practice given in only a few of the ashrams in the Orient. One is in South India, another in the Himalaya Mountains, one in the Katsupari Monastery in the remote Northern Tibetan Mountains, and one in Western China.

The concepts of rejuvenation are based upon the

unique idea that in the body of man (which is a living and functioning organism, independent of the mind yet influenced by it) is a spiritual energy and a *Kal* (negative) energy. These energies are generally kept at a balance during the time of man's life on earth. But as one grows older, the *Kal* energies take over a little at a time until that period of life when the balance is all in its favor, then death occurs.

It is for this reason that man grows old. If his work or the pressures of his daily life are great, this overbalance can come before his normal span of life is finished for this incarnation. If he does not have proper nutrition, a proper attitude on life, nor a proper knowledge about life, this balance can grow more rapidly on the negative side, bringing him to physical death more quickly.

The idea of the *Kaya Kalp* is to increase the span of life by raising the ECK forces in the human body so that the balance will be brought in favor of the positive side of the energies.

The *Kaya Kalp* cure consists of a dieting program in which the only foods eaten are taken directly from the soil and prepared especially for the particular person whose body system is lacking in certain minerals and vitamins. Among these foods are the famous herbs which are known for the restoring of the vital energies of the body.

First is the Pan-Nag, or the Asiatic ginseng, which is called "The Man Plant" by the Chinese. They have used it for over five thousand years as a health tonic and to prolong human life. It is said to help the sick recover, to make the healthy stronger, and to reactivate the entire human organism.

Although this herb has been discussed in another chapter, it is well to point out here that today in China and India men over fifty include it regularly in their diet in order to preserve their virility.

Another rejuvenation herb used in the same system of *Kaya Kalp* is the Gotu-Kola. It is said that a few leaves eaten raw daily will strengthen and revitalize the body and brain. It is supposed to be the essential factor in the extreme age reached by elephants in Ceylon where the herb grows wild.

Gotu-Kola has pale green, fan-shaped leaves and is a ground creeper. When mixed with regular food and served daily in the diet of anyone, health is restored and one is able to live to a ripe old age. It is grown in India, the Islands of the Indian Ocean, and some parts of South Africa. The natives of India use the plant medicinally as a diuretic to stimulate the kidneys and bladder.

Fo-Ti-Tieng is vastly important in the *Kaya Kalp*. Its properties exert a rejuvenating influence on the ductless glands, the healthy functioning of which keeps the brain and body in good health.

Sarsaparilla is used in a limited way. The root, according to reports, contains hormones and is beneficial in bringing about vitality in a person who has lost his ability to reproduce children through disease, accident, or old age.

It is said that three types of hormones are found in the sarsaparilla root. These are the male hormone testosterone, progesterone, and cortin. Various experiments have shown that the administration of testosterone tends to restore the vitality and to bring about mental alertness and physical strength to men who are entering the stage of physical decline. In a sense this hormone prolongs youth and prevents premature aging.

If we want to keep well and have a long life, then it is wise to see what those in charge of the *Kaya Kalp* program do with the diets of their people. They provide the following minerals for those participating in the *Kaya Kalp:*

Lime or calcium salts are found in every tissue. They are particularly essential to the teeth, bones, nails, hair, and muscle development. They improve the stamina, are beneficial to the nerves, and help the pulse.

Phosphorus is likewise essential to the bones, teeth, supple tissues, and to stimulate growth. It is also present in the cell nuclei and vital to the brain.

Iron is vital to the blood. It forms the red pigment, hemoglobin, and assists in the carrying of oxygen from the lungs to the tissues. It also is of importance to metabolism and helps anemia, sallow complexion, poor appetite, and adrenal gland trouble arising from a lack of iron salts in the blood.

Iodine is a food mineral which has been found to be deficient in the modern diet of man. It is essential to the thyroid gland which controls the metabolism of the body and our emotional reactions. Iodine foods prevent goiter, strengthen the nerves, are beneficial in kidney disorders and in adjusting the physique to better proportions when either too fat or too thin.

Manganese plays a part in the process of reproduction, lactation and growth.

Other minerals which help prolong the body's life are potassium and magnesium. They are both essential because of their part in body health similar to the function of calcium salts.

Copper is usually associated with iron in food substances and is essential to its assimilation by the body.

Other items which the *Kaya Kalp* treatment takes up are: physical exercises coordinated to supply blood to every part of the body, special massages, and relaxation exercises for mind and body.

There is an abstinence from social activity while undergoing the treatments. In special mental concentration exercises one learns to develop a calm mental attitude and to clear the mind of all worldly thoughts. Poisonous elements such as worry, temper, and passion are erased from the mind. A determination and will to live longer is developed which is close to self-hypnosis.

The results of the *Kaya Kalp* depend upon the individual. A complete treatment may take a few months or a year. As a result the positive energy is increased, decaying tissues are removed and replaced with the youthfulness and strength of new body energies. The determination to live longer is now a natural part of the character.

Anyone who is able to find and take treatments of the *Kaya Kalp* should increase his life span at least twenty to thirty years. It is found that the health and vigor of one's youthful years will return, gray hair disappear, and he will be able to have children again.

However, one cannot expect to find the places where these treatments are given unless he is willing to serve humanity in some manner. Not everyone is able to take such treatments of the *Kaya Kalp* system, because if this were so, the world might be flooded with all sorts of persons who have longevity, but who take advantage of it by gaining control of communities, states, and nations for their own advantage. The fortunate ones are carefully selected by those in charge.

The same holds true of anyone who is able to visit the spiritual city of Agam Des. These people are only those who have been selected by the ECK Masters to make such trips by Soul Travel. Yaubl Sacabi, the ancient ECK Master in charge of this strange city, does not allow anyone there—even those who might wander upon it by chance. He is probably the oldest of any being who lives on this planet, but he appears to be a man in his late thirties. Occasionally, those who participate in the works of ECK can reach the spiritual city of Agam Des. But again, it is only via the invitation of the ECK Masters that one can reach it and enjoy the works of these strange adepts.

Procaine HCL, better known as H-3, has been used frequently by authorities to help older people regain health and to expand life. It is said that Procaine HCL is non-habit forming, well tolerated in the body, and above all, not a narcotic. It can be bought openly without a prescription.

H-3 was developed in Rumania under government supervision and was first used with older people for treatment of the signs of age. Early experiments were deemed successful, and research has been done in many countries and has progressed into what is known as Gerovital H-3 therapy. It is said that the experiments here in this country have been successful, and some value was found in treating hypertension, irregular heart rhythm, angina pectoris, skin inflammation, hives, and narcotics addiction.

H-3 seems to have been successful in helping the elderly restore memory, energy, hearing, dulled mental facilities, and in treating rheumatism, diseases of the cardiovascular system and the gastro-intestinal system. Apparently, H-3 will be further developed, and in the future, some announcement will be made as to the results of experiments by medical research teams.

Longevity normally belongs in the area of family characteristics. While some families are noted for their long span of life, some are notoriously short. Those living in rural areas where life is slower, tempers are more even, and there is less chance of eating foods which have been processed, are apt to have a greater life span than their city cousins. This has been found to be true in Hunza, where a number of people are advanced in age, but appear to be middle-aged or less. Some persons claiming to be over a hundred years of age are cropping up in remote corners of the world. Lately such reports have been received from the deep rural areas of Russia, as well as Turkey and the Baltic countries.

There are several reasons for this. First, is family stock. If the family stock is strong, tough, and healthy, the body does not weaken and succumb to disease like those who are living under strain and stress in the metropolitan areas. Second, many are living in such deep rural sections of the country that they have to live directly off the land, and the soil of these lands could possibly contain minerals and vitamins which are important to the body. Since food is not so plentiful where people have to raise and cultivate their own food products, it is possible that they do not have so much to eat as in other places. Too often the body is overfed and this creates a problem, for it is more easily weakened and can fall victim to disease and illness. It is best to skimp on food rather than overeat.

Another reason may be that people living in these areas can find plants such as the Pan Nag, the mandrake plant, Fo-Ti-Tieng, and the Gotu-Kola to supplement their nutritional needs. This would, of course, establish greater longevity, and they would naturally retain youth, vitality, and those factors which give the body long life when others are struggling to keep free from sickness and health problems.

In the onrush of civilization, man acquired the idea that he must accumulate possessions by pushing ahead and driving himself into a frenzy. In the process of this he has lost the inner ability to replenish that spiritual self which is the sustainer. Consequently, he has undergone great strain which wears out his bodily strength and resistance. The foods with which he feeds his body lack nourishment, and he has no time to rest, to be silent, to try his spiritual exercises, and to relax. Nervous tension sets in and shortens his life. No man who is easily irritated can have complete peace of mind, because his nerves, muscles, and brain are constantly under great tension.

Therefore, he seeks out healers who work by spirit. This is good, but he must give full consideration to what he is doing. There must be practical sense applied to his finding the right healer who is going to give him back his health, if this is possible. It is the same yardstick by which he would find the right healer in the physical medicine field.

The idealist is drawn toward the mystical and transcendental by his desire to lift the burden of suffering from humanity. He is aware of the limitations of orthodox methods, and he hopes to escape from these limitations. While he does not condemn spiritual healing, he must look very deeply into the whole subject. He cannot shut his eyes to the unsatisfactory and disastrous results that happen when spiritual healing has been ignorantly or inadequately employed.

Good intentions are no substitute for sound knowledge. The satisfactory healer is one who has an adequate knowledge of the physical, psychic, mental, and spiritual nature of man. He must know how they correlate with one another. They fit together like the layers of skin on the body, each essential function in its place.

Even the most extreme spiritual healers do not expect any man to grow a new arm or leg. The greatest mistake that healers make is failing to recognize that each plane has its own laws. They must recognize where the problem lies and work from this plane to help nature take its course.

Other factors, too, enter into healing, such as the Karmic pattern of other lives which may influence the present life and must be worked out. When the Living ECK Master recognizes this in his chela, he stands aside and allows the Karma to work itself out. He can also recognize when one is suffering from strain because of the pressures in his life, or when a lack of proper vitamins, minerals, and proper foods have brought the chela to the edge of a nervous breakdown. Also, he knows there is a time and place for spiritual healing, as well as a time and place for medical treatment. He never interferes with the latter, for medicine has its place.

Spiritual healing has its limitations whether the

161

healer admits it or not. He cannot blatantly tell the victim of some physical, psychic or spiritual problem that, "you are healed," and walk away. He must also consider the spiritual level of the person who approaches him. If he who requests healing has a low survival factor, he is not apt to be healed spiritually.

If he has a chronic negative attitude, it is not likely that anyone can do much for him. However, if he has a positive, cheerful attitude, it is most likely that he can have a healing, which can often be called a miracle.

No healer in his right mind would make a diagnosis of anyone's problems and prescribe, unless it is on a spiritual level. The healer is limited in his work, and if he believes that he has the power to cure anyone who has the breath of life in him, he is apt to be heading straight into trouble. He cannot diagnose and prescribe, because he has not had the background nor the training to do so. He is being naive if he believes that he can heal anyone who comes to him. He must not make rash promises that he can heal anyone who approaches him with a problem.

Nor should he accept anyone who comes to him in regard to relatives, friends, or family members to be healed. Anyone who wants healing should approach the healer personally. The same principle applies here that applies in the physician's office. Nobody goes to the doctor and asks that he treat an absentee patient.

Most people approach the spiritual healer for two reasons. First, they are naive and believe that they can be healed. This is not faith but a sort of a traditional belief that God takes care of anyone who asks. Second, many people are afraid to see their physicians and learn the truth about themselves. A certain percentage want the service of healing without paying or rendering full price for it. Yet they will pay in some way, for this is the way life works.

Chapter Eleven

# HEALTH SECRETS
# OF THE ECK ADEPTS

Those who live the longest and have the most enjoyment of life seem to have a greater amount of intelligence and are more vital in their love, work, and family life than others. For some reason they appear to be wealthier as well.

Married people have longer lives than single, divorced, or widowed people. The active sex life in a marriage appears to give one a stronger survival in the physical body and, of course, animation and vitality. Those who smoke and drink in moderation are going to have a longer life expectancy than those who do so in excess. Those who do not smoke and drink at all will have a far better survival for longevity in the physical body.

Good health is naturally one of the dividends earned as a result of good nutrition and wholesome living from birth to the present time. Good diet will always prolong youth, and whether one is going to have serious illnesses in the twenties, thirties, or fifties of his life depends in large measure upon the choice of food given him from the formative years to his present decade. It can be said that the characteristics of senility may not be the mark of old age, but rather of poor nutrition.

Good nutrition slows the aging process, while poor nutrition accelerates the processes of physiological and psychological aging. Malnutrition can rapidly bring about the appearance of old age. The hair loses its color, the skin wrinkles, and the vital organs develop malfunctions while chemical changes of the body come about.

Magnesium is required for good mentality. It is often called the mineral of life because it is very vital to the core of all the physical makeup of the body. The motor nerves are dependent on magnesium to conduct the electrical impulses from the brain to the muscles. Magnesium makes the difference between the performance of the motor nerves, whether it is going to be slow and labored, or quick, smooth and well-coordinated.

Magnesium also helps to maintain the normal blood pressure needed to build strong bones and teeth. Magnesium dissolves and prevents kidney stones, speeds healing, and helps lower serum cholesterol. Magnesium is the mineral for keeping the memory in good working order. A new pill has been developed called the "memory pill" which has magnesium as its base.

Magnesium, too, regulates the functions of cells other than bones. It gives energy to the vital part of the normal cells because of the oxidation of glucose through the enzymes. The process which activates the enzymes requires magnesium.

This releases a whole chain of action. The enzymes activated by magnesium mediate the movement of muscles, the process of breathing, storage of energy, digestion of food, building of tissues, course of reproduction, workings of the brain and even the thought processes, are the results of the activating force of this particular mineral.

If anyone is living in a metropolitan area where the water has been artificially fluoridated, more magnesium intake is needed. The best source of magnesium is dolomite, nuts, sunflower and pumpkin seeds.

Vitamin E is a stop gap for the aging process in the body. It prevents oxygen from combining with the essential fatty acids to form peroxides and a process called free radicals. The latter causes the cells to die and impede the action of the important enzymes. The body energy lessens, and the body's ability to renew itself is diminished. One begins to age in body and face.

Should the consumption of fats outbalance the amount of Vitamin E available, we have another youthful vitamin, Vitamin C, stepping in. Vitamin C works like a cleansing process, sweeping up the troublesome free radicals which are formed from too much fat consumption, breaking them down and eliminating them through the body's natural elimination system. This is why one needs more Vitamin C as he grows older.

Vitamin C joins forces with Vitamin E to help in the prevention of the peroxides. But there must always be enough Vitamin C in the intake of the daily diet, or in supplementary amounts, to be effective on two lines of battle against old age. It plays both an offensive and defensive role for the body's health.

Another way to a happy old age is that of the nucleic acids. These are mysterious, almost magical substances, which are an essential part of the genetic process and participate in the renewal of the body cells.

These acids relate to a longer life free of degenerative disease and to that quality of feeling young as long as the individual lives. The nucleic acids are the cellular components which control heredity and the subsequent ability of the body to keep reproducing its inherited patterns of life.

The Pharaohs of ancient Egypt formed a closed shop on outsiders, marrying their own sisters and cousins to keep the throne intact. But the genetic defects of the family kept reproducing in subsequent generations. Therefore, the successors to the throne were usually the children of the non-royal wives.

The greatest of the Pharaohs was Tuthmosis II, who expanded his empire beyond the boundaries of those kings before him. Like his father, he was an illegitimate child. The most famous of the Pharaohs was Amenhotep IV, the son of a Nubian mother who was a court woman without any rank of royalty. He is known to us as the first Pharaoh who tried to establish a single God. He also founded a new capital and new laws. In tradition he married his mother, his cousin (the famous Egyptian beauty, Nefertiti), and his daughter. But Tutankhamen, the son who succeeded him and the only surviving heir to the throne, was by an unrelated wife, a non-royalist. Marriages of this type did not produce longevity, for the nucleic acids known to science as DNA and RNA, which should renew themselves and keep their patterns of genetic information as clear and distinct as possible, cannot do so in interfamily marriages.

Brewers yeast is said to be one product rich in nucleic acids. Besides yeast, other foods which are rich in these acids are seafoods of all kinds, especially small sardines and herring roe. Organ meats, particularly sweetbreads, help to stop aging in man.

One begins to wonder about the ages of famous people in the past and any possible connection with the soil and sea for nutrition. In looking at the longevity of the famous, we find a list that goes like this (I have set the names down at random): Haydn died at age seventy-seven; Mozart at thirty-five; Beethoven at fifty-seven; Goethe at eighty-three; Schubert at thirty-one; Mendelssohn at thirty-eight; Wordsworth at eighty; Coleridge at sixty-two; Keats at twenty-six; and Shelley at thirty.

Interesting figures when one compares this list with the ages of some ancient personalities: Aeschylus died at seventy-one; Sophocles at ninety-one; Euripides at seventy-eight; Aristophanes at seventy; Socrates at eighty-seven; Plato at ninety-eight; Isocrates at ninety-five; Gorgias at seventy; and Protagoras at seventy-six.

Shelley was drowned by accident, but Aeschylus

and Euripides both met with accidental deaths. Socrates was executed, and Protagoras died in a shipwreck.

What does the above have to do with nutrition? The Greeks named seemed in those days to have lived mostly on bread, a few olives, barley meal, a little wine, and fish. Yet this diet seems to have bred a vigorous race of men.

One is astonished at the longevity of those who lived in the past. One of the great historical figures of Greece was Empedocles, a statesman and philosopher, whom according to the *Lives of Philosophers* by Diogenes Laertius, lived to be one hundred fifty. Sophocles composed his magnificent *Oedipus Coloneus* at age ninety. Agesilaus, King of Sparta, directed and led his army in the field at age eighty. Socrates changed the current of human thought without writing a word, without preaching a doctrine, simply by talking in the streets of Athens, which he left but twice in defense of the city.

It is possible that the ancient Greeks received the right minerals, vitamins, and nucleic acids from fish, and the necessary Vitamin E from fish and whole grains. Their bread was made directly from wheat gathered in fields without any processing. Grapes furnished a source of Vitamin C. Seeds and berries also likely furnished the rest of what was needed for the body supply of Vitamin C for longevity.

One traditional medicine is still relied upon in Japan which is called *Kampo*. It originated in the tradition of Chinese medicine, which prescribes concoctions prepared from plants, leaves, grass, and roots.

*Kampo* is entirely different from modern medicine, especially from the standpoint of diagnostics or conception of the human body. Modern medicine is based on scientific analysis, while *Kampo* depends upon the practitioner's intuition.

The physician in *Kampo* tries to grasp the

condition of the patient in a whole view. It is the nature of the Eastern philosopher to adapt himself to the whole instead of to parts. This is the way that he is trained from childhood. Whatever he would prescribe for the patient would be prepared from grass, leaves, tree trunks, bark, roots, and herbs. These are all natural products, but the portions vary according to the complaint.

Until modern medicines were introduced into Japan, only the technique of *Kampo* was used. It has suffered somewhat the same results as many elements of Japanese culture and has been partly forgotten by some of the newer generations. But in the past few years it has become popular again, for many people of Japan are seeking out *Kampo* practitioners.

The *Kampo* physician inspects the patient by his own intuition and feelings. He is generally one who has had many years of experience and an unusual skill, as well as a sharp medical intuition.

The examination includes four separate points. These are: questions, visual examination, tactual examination, and smell. The *Kampo* physician accepts everything the patient says as part of the examination. His whole analysis is based upon the subjectiveness of what is learned beyond the objective or scientific examination given by the Western physician. The *Kampo* doctor listens to the patient, obtains information about his family, his medical history, living conditions, environment, and anything which can add to the knowledge needed for diagnosis. At the same time, he is giving the patient a physical checkup.

When the examination is finished he determines the proper treatment through the application of the method needed. This process is known as "sho," which is the concept unique to *Kampo*. It is not found in Western medicines. The "sho" for the prescription is given in the *Shokanron* a sort of *Kampo* bible, written about two hundred years ago.

The materials which compose *Kampo* prescriptions are natural grasses, plants, and their components. These are crude liquids extracted from complex living matter. The effective ingredients are contained in living medicines, which can be naturally assimilated by the human body. While chemical medicines can cause allergies or irritations, *Kampo* does not do this, according to claims, nor put a burden on the digestive and assimilative organs.

*Kampo* had its origin in the western part of China, south of the Yangtze River. The climatic conditions provided for the natural growth of roots, barks, grasses, and herbs, which were discovered useful to the body some two thousand years ago.

Two books which described the medical treatment of the *Kampo* were both compiled about the year 150 A.D. They are the *Shokanron* and the *Kinki Yoryaku*. The *Shokanron* gives an unrivaled system of clinical medicine, stipulating the right prescriptions for diseases which have their origin in fever. The *Kinki Yoryaku* provides the results of the clinical examination of main chronic symptoms and their respective prescriptions. Both books include all the basic essentials of the modern system of *Kampo*. It was not until about 400 A.D. that such treatments were able to reach across the seas to Japan. The latter country accepted them at once, because of the similarity in climate of the two areas of Asia.

In the beginning *Kampo* was available only to the aristocracy, because of the prices and the small number of doctors who could practice *Kampo*. It was not until the sixteenth century when the middle class began to make itself prominent that *Kampo* became a popular medical treatment among the people. For the next 300 years it made remarkable progress. It was altered many times over from its original Chinese methods and was adapted to the Japanese physical and mental environment.

During the middle of the nineteenth century when

a smallpox plague broke out in Japan, *Kampo* started its downward trend. A vaccine was brought from Holland to curb smallpox and it was miraculously effective in controlling the plague. *Kampo* was unable to cure the victims of smallpox, so Western medicine became popular in Japan.

Two additional aspects of *Kampo* are acupuncture and moxacautery. The basic idea of the two stimulative remedies are explained simply. If a special stimulation is effected on a proper point on the body, the body will respond by changing, and this in turn will have an effect on the locale of the malady. If the stimulant is in excess, the reaction will only have an unfavorable influence on the ailment. However, if the stimulant is just right, it will promote the body's inherent power to cure and facilitate its own recovery.

Acupuncture stimulates the body by thrusting a pointed needle into the flesh. The needle is made of gold, silver, iron, or imitation platinum. It is very thin and ranges from 0.17 to 0.3. The process is not at all painful if the acupuncturist is an experienced practitioner.

The method for the thrust of the needle into the skin varies. It can be slight, deep, kept in a long time or momentarily, removed by flipping, pushing and pulling repeatedly. It can be inserted vertically or slanted. Acupuncture has been introduced into the mid-European countries where it is under study.

Moxacautery is the method of giving thermal stimulation on the skin. Moxa is the white part of the back of mug wort leaves obtained after drying and pounding. The moxa, which is easy to handle, burns instantly and evenly. It varies in size with the application, but the usual size is about the size of a grain of rice. The burning temperature for moxa is from 60 degrees C to 100 degrees C, and it can be increased by fanning to control the stimulation. The scientific value of moxacautery is said to improve the blood circulation and increase the white corpuscles.

The points at which to apply these local stimulation remedies have been fixed by thousands of years of experience. The vital points are known as *keitetsu* and are located on the external surface of the body, on the face, palms, and even the soles of the feet. They are divided into groups and linked by tracks called *keiraku*. The *keiraku* plays an important role in the treatment. By locating related tracks—*keiraku*—a toothache can be cured through the stimulation of the points in the limbs. Stomach ache and gallstones can be dealt with by stimulating points on the back.

Although *Kampo* is not as effective as modern medicine, especially in social, preventive, and surgical areas, it can effect treatments impossible to modern medicines. No *Kampo* school of instruction is available. One has to learn under a *Kampo* practitioner and learn the *Kampo* techniques singularly. The main area where these trainees fail is the lack of objectivity in their working with patients. This is the reason why *Kampo* does not have a place with modern Western medicines. It cannot be transmitted by textbooks and its scriptures alone. Its fatal flaw lies in the lack of its ability to reach any objectivity.

When we speak of spiritual healing, we mean the healing of the spirit within, which is expressed outwardly and visibly as improved physical conditions. In many instances this is the curing of disease or the healing of injuries. It does not mean anything magical, as many people think. It is a spontaneous thing which reaches out from the healer and touches the victim, making him whole again.

Those on the spiritual path of ECK wonder if transplants of organs from one person to another is complying with the laws of nature. Human organ transplants may not be exactly proper for man. Few have succeeded, for the tissues of the organs of one person are not the same as of another.

171

According to the cosmic law, the human body cannot accept parts of another human body as repair for itself. This is true especially in the heart area. The chemical essence of the mechanisms are not alike and may often be injurious to one another. The wavelengths, too, can be wrong and may create disharmony in the body which is using the transplant. Whatever the life length of the body, it should live on its own and not from parts of another, like a worn out automobile which has been patched together with parts from a junk yard.

Longevity should be within the same body, with its own body parts, working together with the same rhythmic cycle as from birth. Unless we keep these parts healthy and within ourselves as the original vital organs, we will never have anything that appears to be long life.

We live in power tides and cycles, but few seem to know this, and until we begin to learn this, suffering will be our lot.

These tides and cycles are part of the cosmogony which are the relative movements of the complicated system of planetary chains and rounds, races, and sub-races. In other words, we have tides of power which lift one race above the other in the history of the world, and cycles which affect this particular race's affairs while in power. This is also true of the individual, and he must learn how to live with these tides of power and cycles. Within the races these cycles or rounds of the orbits come about the fourth through the sixth generation, but it depends on the original stock of the founders and related peoples. If the race stays together, it is possible for an empire or a nation to last for many generations. As long as each group, family, and race holds together as a tight cell in society, they are practically invincible.

These cycles of nature which strike the individual, family, groups, and races are cycles of the peak of power tides or extreme good health, happiness and prosperity, or the opposite.

The destruction of a family's longevity can come about through vice and dissipation, which leads to a downgrading of health and satisfactory old age. Anyone who is low in his mental and physical health will naturally go lower when the psychic and physical cycles of the negative types hit him.

The greatest vices which can bring about the downfall of a family are drugs and alcohol. We have plenty of knowledge, research, and communication on the results of drug abuse, but few people pay much attention. Users find a way of getting their thrills without having to go to hard drugs. For example, they find the injection of Kool-Aid powder into the vein will give them a drug-like effect. Nutmeg is said to produce the same effect when properly prepared. Sniffing such common household items as turpentine, paint remover, nail polish, and gasoline are listed among the items named which seem to produce an effect similar to marijuana.

People can play dangerous games with their health under different circumstances at almost any time. It comes back to the one thing which is basic in all life: we are responsible to a large degree for maintaining our health. We are aware that LSD can affect the chromosomes and genes. Most drugs tend to be damaging to the brain cells, and more than one pleasure seeker has died from the aftereffects of a session with drugs.

Man does not understand that so much of his physical health will originate in other planes—the astral, causal, mental or Soul regions. All he can think about is that some biochemist's medicine will cure his ailments, or that a psychologist is going to clear his mental realm of its aberrations.

What we are mainly concerned with here is the health guidance given by the ECK Masters, the most reliable source for wisdom in any aspect of life. So often the information from the astral plane tells us that fasting, ascetic practices, and certain foods are best for health or spiritual growth. The ECK Masters have never gone in for any unreasonable austerities or fads in spiritual unfolding. They have always been quite reluctant to advise the average person in any of these areas because of the matter of health. Drugs and Alcohol are certainly on the list of those things which are not needed by any ECK chela, nor anyone else. This is not so much the question of Karma as it is of keeping the mind clear and the body in good health. It is considered a part of one's spiritual responsibility to keep his body in good condition, so that he can do his best work, using the body as an instrument. For this reason the Living ECK Master always says that none are to abuse the body in any way, but to keep it in perfect health and in good tone. The physical body is man's important instrument in working out his salvation and his liberation from the Wheel of the Eighty-Four.

The popular illusion today is that the drug addict and the saint are reaching for the same experience. The addict is looking for thrills, whereas the saint is seeking the wondrous glories of God. What the addict finds is generally the lower astral plane, which does not seem to harbor much of anything other than wonders of the lower entities and some colors. Many of those who have been seeking a true experience of God have gone through such things and believed they had received the true glories. Many a mystic and many a saint, if one divides the categories, have had experiences in the psychic worlds, the astral, causal, and mental, then had the same problems, thereafter. Each believed that he found the true heavenly kingdom.

This is the reason I have always discouraged drugs. It is a false area which the addict is led to, and he is certainly not under his own control. Furthermore, it is also detrimental to his health. When one sacrifices health in his youth, it is certain that he will not have it thereafter during his life spent on earth.

Our biggest problem is that we seldom know what is wrong with ourselves. That is, the physicians and health experts are so busy, and it is almost impossible to sit down and talk out our health problems with them. And in many cases it might be best not to discuss such matters. This is the same problem that the Living ECK Master has with so many people who are trying to bypass physical plane living and enter into the heavenly worlds in hopes of healing, good health and a full purse. If he said what was really on his mind then it might defeat the individual completely. That person might go into a deep depression and not be able to pull out of it. In other words, it is best not to say anything at particular times because of such reactions.

This is not a question of being dishonest with the consultee but it is a matter of perhaps giving him a little longer to live by not putting a certain amount of worry into his mind.

Then again, if telling the afflicted that something is wrong arouses him into some action to take care of himself, the information can be given out to suit the purpose all or in parts. It depends on the person and his nature as to whether he should have full knowledge of what his ailments might be.

It is said that one of the best foods we can eat is an egg. Eggs contain both cholesterol and its synergist. Eggs also contain lecithin in abundance. They are easily obtained and easy for anyone to cook. However, it is best to have them hard-boiled, soft-boiled, or poached. Fried eggs are hard to digest if cooked in bacon grease or butter. Eggs are probably the most nutritious staple food available to man. Milk is claimed to be the second most nutritious food, according to certain health authorities. Liver, lean meats, and cottage cheese are rated high among nutritious foods.

If one is thinking of dieting to lose weight, he will find that problems arise. For example, take the all-protein diet in which one has an intake of lean meats and supposedly little fats and carbohydrates. The whole problem here, if one is not careful, is the drinking of water to flush out the daily waste matter of the body. Some of these diets call for eight ten-ounce glasses of water daily. This diet will take off weight, but one must be careful not to let the vitamin and mineral balance of his body be disturbed on such a regimen. He should consume vitamin complex tablets daily along with a mineral complex, in order to keep up this balance within his body. Otherwise, the diet does him little good, because he is losing these all important essentials and his health will decrease. This is why anyone who wishes to diet should be careful to watch other things which might be injurious to his health.

Old age can be reversed in many people. A strong regimen of vitamin injections, good nutrition, vitamin supplements and minerals can alter the processes of old age. When the aging of the glands, especially the pituitary, is halted or reversed, one begins to feel the turn toward youth again. The feeling of persecution which comes with old age is given up, and the individual starts thinking of things to do. Gray hair and wrinkles start falling away and in their place come glossy hair, smooth and wrinkleless skin, the signs of youth.

But to have youth, one must also have will power and imagination, using both to secure a place in a world which assesses the energies of younger people more fit for performance.

## Chapter Twelve

## HEALTH AS AN AID
## IN SPIRITUAL GROWTH

Those who are vitally interested in health should try to keep to an all-purpose diet consisting of essential nerve-building vitamins, blood-building minerals, gland stimulating protein, and the hormone-nourishing unsaturated fatty acids, as well as all other necessary ingredients which give good health to the body.

Illness or disease is created by multiple causes. We seldom think about the individual activities of the cells and groups of cells. When one has a stomach ache he wants it relieved quickly as possible. But we do know that the body cells are kept in good health by the ingress of inorganic cell-salts.

The mineral salts are very important to functional activities in the cells of the human body. According to bio-chemists, there are several tissue cell-salts which are necessary to the human body, either to ward off illnesses or to maintain general good health.

These tissue cell-salts are as follows: (1) Calcarea Fluoride (Fluoride of Lime); (2) Calcarea Phosphate (Phosphate of Lime); (3) Calcarea Sulphate (Sulphate of Lime); (4) Ferrum Phosphate (Phosphate of Iron); (5) Kali Muriate (Chloride of Potash); (6) Kali Phosphate (Phosphate of Potash); (7) Kali Sulphate (Sulphate of Potash); (8) Magnesia Phosphate (Phosphate of Magnesia); (9) Natrum Muriate (Chloride of Soda); Natrum Sulphate (Sulphate of Soda); and (10) Silicea (Silica). These were isolated by intense research by Dr. W.H. Schuessler a number of years ago, and his analysis seems to have been successful.

The function activated by each of these salts balances the physiological needs of the body and its vital organs and tissues. If the body does not have the proper intake of various mineral salts in the daily diet, the mineral imbalance will cause certain disorders.

The mineral salts named above act upon the physical system in various ways:

Calcarea Fluoride is found in the surface of the bones, in the enamel of the teeth, and in the elastic fibres of the skin, muscular tissue, and blood vessels. Calcarea Fluoride is said to be the remedy for diseases affecting the surface of the bones and the enamel of the teeth. A deficiency of Calcarea Fluoride results in a loosened condition of the elastic fibers, including dilatation of the blood vessels, hemorrhoids, varicose veins, hardened glands, and cracks in the skin.

Calcarea Phosphate is a constitutent of the bones, teeth, connective tissue, blood corpuscles and the gastric juices. It unites with the organic substance albumin, giving solidity to the bones, building the teeth, and entering into the secretions of the body, like the blood and gastric juices. Bone structure is fifty-seven percent Calcarea Phosphate, and without it no bone can be formed.

Calcarea Phosphate uses albumin as a cement to build bone structure. It enters into the formation of teeth which makes it a good supplement in childhood to build good teeth. It also plays an important part in assimilation and digestion. It is closely allied with Magnesia Phosphate and is frequently given in alternation with it as a remedy in some ailments.

Calcarea Phosphate is used to treat bone diseases, whether inherited or due to nutritional defectiveness. It aids the union of fractured bones and is a remedy in anemia and chlorosis when the teeth are growing. It also is a remedy for building up new blood corpuscles after an acute disease.

Calcarea Sulphur is found in the epithelial skin cells and in the blood. It is a preventive of cell disintegration and suppuration. A deficiency of Calcarea Sulphur allows suppuration to continue, and wounds that are slow to heal. It works well with Silicea in healing of catarrhs, boils, ulcers, etc.

Ferrum Phosphate is a remedy for inflammatory and feverish conditions. It is found in the blood where it gives the corpuscles their reddish color. It gives strength to the walls of the arteries and blood vessels. Ferrum phosphate is said to be the most essential cell salt of all, for it is thought to be the healing agency for body inflammation. It is also used in cases of abnormal conditions of the blood corpuscles, and in cases of trouble with muscular tissue.

Kali Muriate unites with albumin and forms fibrin, which is found in every tissue of the body with exception of the bones. A deficiency of this cell salt will cause a discharge of a white, thick, sticky substance from the mucous membranes and a heavy white or gray coating of the tongue.

Kali Muriate is also a remedy for catarrhal conditions, and it is used in controlling spasmodic croup, diarrhea, and bronchitis. In conditions associated with deficiency of Kali Muriate, the blood tends to thicken and form clots. Kali Muriate is often referred to as the liver salt, because of its action on this vital organ of the body. It helps maintain the fluidity of the blood and it stimulates the flow of the bile.

Kali Phosphate is the component of all the tissues and fluids of the body, mostly of the brain and nerve cells. It is known to be one of the best nutrients of the nervous system, and it has an antiseptic action which hinders decay of the tissues.

A deficiency of Kali Phosphate produces brain fatigue, mental depression, irritability, fearfulness, timidity, lack of nervous energy. It is good in restoring muscular debility, following acute diseases which are associated with distribution of nervous energies to the vital organs. One of the most prominent symptoms of a deficiency of Kali Phosphate is prostration, along with sluggish conditions of the mind and an exhausted mental state following exertion or emotional strain.

Kali Sulphate is a carrier of oxygen to the cells of the skin. The oxygen in the lungs is taken up by the iron in the blood and carried to every cell in the body by the respective actions of Kali Sulphate and Ferrum Phosphate.

A deficiency of Kali Sulphate will cause a lack of oxygen in the skin and in the epithelial cells and will give rise to symptoms of chilliness, shifting inflammatory pain, and a desire for cool air. Kali Sulphate is a remedy for skin troubles. It promotes perspiration, handles dandruff problems, catarrh of the stomach and bowels, and diarrhea.

Magnesia Phosphate is an anti-spasmodic and works chiefly with the delicate white nerve-fibers of the nerves and muscles. It uses albumin and water to form the transparent fluid which nourishes these fibers.

A deficiency of Magnesia Phosphate in the fiber allows it to contract, to produce spasms and cramps. When this contraction takes place there is pressure on the sensory nerves which gives rise to sharp, shooting, darting or neuralgic pains in any part of the body.

Natrum Muriate is the constituent of every liquid and solid part of the body. It regulates the degree of moisture in the cells by virtue of its property of attracting and distributing water. The body is composed of about seventy percent water, which in the absence of Natrum Muriate would be inert and useless. Any deficiency of the cell salt causes an imbalance of water in the human organism. The patient will have a watery, bloated appearance, will

180

be languid, drowsy, and inclined to have a dulled mental outlook on life.

Natrum Muriate also regulates the quantity of water entering into the composition of the blood corpuscles. Natrum Muriate also controls the production of hydrochloric acid, regulates the density of the fluids which surround the tissue cells, and promotes the activity of changes in the tissues.

Natrum Phosphate is necessary to the blood, muscles, nerves, and the intercellular fluids. It also splits up the lactic acid into carbonic acid and water, and it is the specialized remedy where there is an excess of acid in the system. Any acid condition in the body system gives rise to rheumatism, digestive upsets, intestinal disorders, and has an adverse effect upon the assimilation of food in the body. Natrum Phosphate helps regulate the consistency of bile and is good in treating colic, sick headaches, and gastric disturbances.

One of the functions of Natrum Phosphate is that of assisting in the absorption of water, which is quite different from that of Natrum Muriate, which distributes water, and Natrum Sulphate, which eliminates surplus water from the body. The presence of these three tissue salts in the body control the manner in which the body fluids behave.

Natrum Phosphate serves to emulsify the fatty acids which irritate the digestive system after too many fatty or greasy foods. It corrects gastric troubles in small children who suffer from an excess of lactic acid from milk and sugar.

Natrum Sulphate is found only in the intercellular fluids. Its principal function is to regulate the quantity of water in the tissues, blood, and fluids of the body. It has an attachment for water, and it eliminates any excess from the bile.

Natrum Sulphate splits the lactic acid into carbonic acid and water, leaving a residue of water to be removed from the body system. At the same time,

Natrum Sulphate starts removing the excess water from the body.

A lack of Natrum Sulphate will create an excess of bile flow, jaundice, biliousness, and diarrhea. Such symptoms are irritated by the use of water in any form, that is, by living in low, marshy places, damp buildings, basements, or by eating water plants, fish, and similar foods.

Silicea is found abundantly in the vegetable kingdom, especially in grasses, grains, and palms. It is present in the blood, bile, skin, hair, and nails. It is also a constituent of the connective tissue, bones, nerve sheaths, and mucous membranes. A lack of it shows up when there is a deficient assimilation of food in the body.

One of the secrets of recharging the body lies in an uncooked raw fruit and vegetable diet. The Japanese people, who seem to have a longevity greater than ours as a race, eat a great deal of raw fish. A diet of this nature with raw fruit and vegetables can revitalize the entire system of the human body.

There are many Japanese who believe in a vegetarian diet. During the eighth to the eleventh centuries, the Buddhist religion, which had a strong hold on the Japanese, forbade the killing and eating of animal flesh. Despite this decree, people consumed much fish and bird meat, with a few vegetables. Later, with the spread of Zen during the twelfth century, the eating of vegetables, both raw and cooked, supplemented with fish became prominent in the Japanese diet.

This is quite like the ECK diet, which has been used in the Katsupari monastery in Northern Tibet. Because the emphasis is put upon raw foods, cooked vegetables, fish and poultry, fruits and seeds, many of the diseases which inflict modern man, such as stomach ulcer, arteriosclerosis and cancer, are unheard of among those who are in the monastery.

They acquire vegetables, herbs, vitamins, and minerals from their true sources.

Raw fish, especially the way the Japanese prepare it in *sashimi,* a sauce, is a good, nutritious protein. It is also easy for almost any age to digest.

The best types of fish served raw in Japan are: First, river fish—Carp, Crucian, Trout. Second, the best in the sea—Bonito, Flounder, Mullet, Mackerel, Pompano, Sea Bream, Snipe fish, Squid, Tuna, and Yellowtail. Third, the shellfish served raw in Japan are the Arc-shell, Clam, Cockle, Abalone, Oyster, and Crab.

It is never advisable to eat raw fish except at a good restaurant where it has been properly prepared. Parasites can be eliminated by a skillful cook. No public restaurant in Japan is allowed to operate without health department licenses, so generally one can be safe in eating raw fish there; but to try to prepare raw fish in one's own home is not at all good, for there are always dangers in both allergies and parasites.

An excellent meal which the Japanese serve as a light, simple snack or luncheon is called *ochazuke,* a tasty dish of rice steeped in tea with seaweed on top. Seaweed is a good food somewhat neglected in the Western world, but we are gradually learning that the sea furnishes many more vitamins, herbs, and minerals than we formerly believed.

The reason why most people are tired is that they lack enzymes in their bodies. The food which they eat cannot be digested and utilized, and instead, becomes waste matter and turns to toxins and poisons.

Enzymes offer the key to longevity. These invisible workers seem to be able to neutralize the basic causes of aging in the body and help retain its youthful qualities. The best way of putting enzymes into the body is to eat fruit, properly grown vegetables, certain meats and grain, and seeds.

It has been found that vinegar and spice-laden dressings used on salads, generally destroy or render the enzymes useless. Enzymes are also destroyed in the processing and canning of various vegetables and meats.

Wheat kernels contain the important enzymes of amylase and protease. Grinding the wheat into flour does not harm the enzymes, but the heat used in baking the flour into bread does destroy them. Butter has no enzymes, because the heat used to pasteurize the cream from which it is made destroys them. Canned juices may be rich in vitamins, but the enzymes were destroyed when the juices were heated and poured into the cans. Generally, breakfast foods have few enzymes which have survived the roasting, baking, and packing.

All sugars, including the variety known as raw sugar, do not have many enzymes, because sugar is subjected to a prolonged boiling. The original cane sugar is rich in enzymes, but these disappear when sugar is boiled for human consumption.

We treat our animals better than ourselves, because they get raw products to eat, including cane stalks, while we get processed products. Boiling potatoes, meat, and leafy vegetables in water will bring about a complete destruction of enzymes.

Life could not exist without enzymes. Enzymes digest all of the food to make it small enough to pass through the minute pores of the intestines into the blood. Enzymes rebuild the prepared foods into muscle, nerve, bone, or gland. They assist in storing excess food in the liver or muscles for future use. They are concerned in the formation of urea to be eliminated in the urine, in the elimination of carbon dioxide from the lungs, and in many other important body functions.

Another enzyme helps fix iron in the red blood cells. One enzyme causes coagulation of the blood and stops bleeding. Another decomposes poisonous hydrogen peroxide and liberates healthy oxygen from it. Another enzyme promotes oxidation, the union of oxygen with other substances. Enzymes can change proteins into fat or sugar, or carbohydrates into fat.

Enzymes can live for many years in the dormant state. They have been found to retain their activity for hundreds of years. Enzymes have been found in Egyptian mummies at least 3,000 years old and in the flesh of ancient mammoths buried in graves of ice and snow reckoned to be 50,000 years old.

It is important that one understands that longevity is based upon the enzymes. Much study is being poured into the subject by medical researchers the world over. Enzymes cannot be seen even with the most powerful microscope, and their presence and strength can be determined only by intricate tests.

Good diet is a proper cure for depression cycles, said to be the world's most widespread emotional illness. Depression cycles are said to hit more than four of five million people yearly in the United States alone. The most common symptoms are sadness, constant fatigue, loss of interest in social life, self-neglect, and insomnia. People who are affected with depression cycles in an extreme way and who find themselves in what can be said to be an emotional binge, should take a good look at their diet.

It has been reported that these depressions may be the manifestation of deficiencies of Vitamin B12. The average person can help to offset Vitamin B12 deficiency by eating brewer's yeast and liver.

Another culprit responsible for depressive states and similar illnesses is the low blood sugar problem. The most important nutrient required by the brain is glucose, a sugar, and when it is not available, depression appears. It is a paradox, but too much sugar in the diet makes for a low blood sugar problem in the body. When too many sweets are eaten, the blood becomes loaded with sugar and may cause diabetes.

185

In place of excessive sweets and starches, one can change his diet to include fresh broccoli, brussels sprouts, cabbage, cauliflower, carrots, and similar vegetables. He can also eat unsweetened fruits, such as apples, apricots, berries, grapefruits, bananas. Sugar-rich soft drinks should be cut off the list, along with coffee, because caffeine affects the sugar metabolism of the body.

Another problem of a similar nature can be a depressed state in which the patient hears voices, becomes tense, nervous, and fatigued. Some times doctors put the person with such problems on Niacin or Vitamin B3, and the difficulty clears up in a relatively short period of time. Others have stated that vitamins C, B1, B6, B12, and folic acid will have taken care of this problem.

Oftentimes when people are burdened with the negative emotions, niacin and other Vitamin B nutrients will resolve the dour attitude. It is known among health authorities that illnesses of this nature can result when either environmental factors or chemicals produced in the body upset the ratio of various molecules carried by the blood to the brain. Any deficiency of nutrients needed to nourish the brain can also cause an imbalance in the body and mind.

It is the opinion of some that the proper functioning of the brain requires the right chemicals in the right amounts. The kind of chemical molecules which make up the brain's activities, along with the nervous system's health, have an incredibly significant influence upon the functions of these organs. Most people are aware that a mere speck of LSD entering the bloodstream through the stomach will radically upset the functions of the brain for at least twelve hours.

This is why I have spoken against fasting and other particular ideas which concern the nutrition of the body. If one is deficient in several nutrients which are necessary for the body health, it is possible that he can fall into psychoneurosis and similar types of emotional disturbances. For example, it is claimed that a lack of thiamine can bring ideas of persecution, mental confusion, and bad memory. A deficiency of riboflavin can cause depression, visual disturbance, disordered thinking, and inability to concentrate. A lack of niacin may result in unreasonable fears, anxiety, mania, hallucinations, and dementia. Insufficient pyridoxine may bring on convulsions and irritability.

All important food factors—proteins, nucleic acids, all the vitamins, minerals, and enzymes—work together to help keep man more youthful, regardless of his age.

According to important studies, the vitamin which one can most depend upon to help him avoid the hallmarks of old age, loss of teeth, shrinking in stature, wrinkling of skin, and other symptoms of that dreaded thing we know as old age is said to be the Vitamin C.

While Vitamin E is considered one of the best for keeping the body in good shape, it is now believed that Vitamin C is likely to be of great help in aiding the body to renew itself. This vitamin gives strength to the body to resist and to recover from the destructive attacks of disease.

More Vitamin C is needed as one gets older. It is a requisite for the formation of collagen, an essential protein in teeth, bone cartilage, connective tissue and skin. The need for regenerating collagen is the prime reason that Vitamin C requirements increase with age.

Some people need more vitamins, minerals, and enzymes than others. The mistake which nutritionists make as a fundamental error is attempting to set up a uniform standard for all people. It is not possible to put everybody on a standard diet, and this may be the cause of breakdowns in the physical systems of many people who try to follow such standards. What is one man's poison is another man's meat, so the old saying goes. Each person must study himself and see just what is best for his own body and mind on a daily intake of foods, and which will give him the best nutrients to benefit his energy and good living capacity.

One of the things which many people do not understand is that chronic bowel problems brought on by poor choice of foods is a major cause of varicose veins, according to reports from health authorities. In Britain at least ten percent of the population suffers from varicose veins. This means that one should look to the simplicity of diets having reasonable amounts of meats, fish, poultry, fresh eggs, wholemeal bread, nuts, raisins, salads, and vegetables.

Most people's physical and diet problems started when they were children, especially at school-age. Those who ate large amounts of sweets were bound to eat little else, and the lack of good food soon began to show itself in weakness and disease. When they reached middle-age or old age, their difficulties became more prominent, unless there had been an attempt to remedy the situation.

One will not be able to bring about results over-night through correction of diet. Although there can be some immediate improvement, the dramatic changes will usually take longer than most people will want to wait. Only patience and proper diet will bring results.

In their children's formative years, parents have a great influence which must be channeled toward giving the children good eating habits. These habits can keep them healthy through their respective lives. Since parents are the source of their children's food supply, the parents must give them only what they should have. Apples must be shown to be better for snacks than a piece of cake. Let the child drink fruit juice instead of soda. If this can be done, at least half of the battle to get the child to eat good, nourishing food is won. At least it will give him an early chance to learn how to make selections of foods which will preserve his good health.

Many things have been left unsaid in this book. Good health is every man's right, but no man will keep it if he is careless as to what he feeds his body and mind daily.

# INDEX

## A

Aaron's Beard 120
Aaron's Rod 113
Acid-alkaline balance 27, 29, 65, 142
Acorns 69
Acupuncture 170
Adam and Eve Root 9
Adrenal Gland 157
Aggressiveness 84
Alcohol 18, 73, 77, 131, 134, 174
Alder 13, 123
Alfalfa 53, 55, 60, 61
Alkanet 9, 11
Allergy 169
All-Heal 121
Allopathics 22
Almonds 29, 36, 52, 75, 136
Alum Root 10
Aluminum 56, 62
Amino Acid 31, 61, 75, 109, 112
Amulet 9, 16
Anemia 27, 28, 56, 60, 73, 92, 157, 179
Anesthetic 117
Anise 10, 41, 71, 72, 113
Anger 76
Angelica Root 10, 13, 41
Anthelmintic Herbs 9
Antibiotic 22, 72
Antispasmodics 7, 41, 42, 64, 66, 122, 124, 128, 129, 179, 180
Antiperiodic 129
Antiseptic 113, 117, 139, 180
Anxiety 111, 124, 133, 187
Aperient 64, 129
Aphrodisiac 7
Appetite 61, 79, 134, 135, 141, 145, 157
Apples 29, 36, 51, 62, 136, 186, 188
Apricots 29, 36, 43, 136, 186

Aromatics 7, 10, 41, 71, 116, 117, 125, 150
Arteries 57, 58, 60, 179
Arthritis 55, 140
Artichokes 41
Ascorbic Acid 127
Ash 72
Asparagus 64, 90, 136
Aster 42
Asthma 55, 57, 72
Astringent 7, 9, 10, 17, 19, 42, 62, 113, 119, 125, 128, 130
Atlantis 37, 40, 41, 42, 43
Atma 50
Attachment 84
Attitude 157, 162
Augue Weed 129
Ayur Vedha 96, 154

## B

B-Complex 30
Back 73, 86
Bacteria 15, 31, 84
Balm 16, 66, 125, 126
Balm of Gilead 11
Bananas 146, 186
Barley 39, 167
Barberry 104, 122
Basil 41
Bay Laurel 117
Beans 8, 18, 27, 31, 41, 52, 60, 84, 101, 136, 137
Beef 31, 39, 41, 87, 136, 149
Beer 59
Beets 28, 29, 30, 55
Berries 167, 186
Betel Nut 9, 73
Bethroot 11, 13
Bhavachakra 133
Bile 30, 57, 179, 181, 182
Bioflavin 127
Biology 87
Black Alder 10
Blackberry 10, 13
Blackstrap 145
Bladder 64, 72, 88, 110, 113, 116, 156
Bleeding 65, 125

190

193

195

198

# GLOSSARY

ANODYNE:            Eases pain.

ANTHELMINTIC:       Rids the body of tapeworms and parasites.

ANTIPERIODIC:       Prevents periodic return of severe symptoms in disease as intermittent fever.

ANTISPASMODIC:      Prevents or allays spasms or cramps. Relieves muscular irritability.

APERIENT:           A mild laxative or cathartic.

AROMATIC:           Used to make other drugs more palatable and has a fragrant smell and pungent taste.

ASTRINGENT:         Contracts tissue.

CARMINATIVE:        Prevents griping pain in cathartics. Rids the body of stomach and intestinal gas.

CATHARTIC:          Aperient, laxative or purgative. Causes evacuation from the bowels.

DEMULCENT:          Soothes membranes of the nose and throat and helps coughs and colds.

DIAPHORETIC:        Induces sweating.

| | |
|---|---|
| **DIURETIC:** | Flushes the kidneys and promotes the secretion of urine when the kidneys are not active enough. |
| **EMETIC:** | Induces vomiting. |
| **EMMENAGOGUE:** | Encourages the menstrual flow. |
| **EXPECTORANT:** | Modifies quality and quantity of the mucous secretions and favors its expulsion in cases of colds and coughs and irritations of the throat. |
| **LAXATIVE:** | Stimulates secretion of the intestinal glands and excites the movement of the bowels. |
| **NERVINE:** | Soothes the nerves. |
| **PECTORAL:** | Relieves afflictions of the chest and lungs. |
| **PURGATIVE:** | Strong laxative. |
| **SEDATIVE:** | Calms the nerves. |
| **STOMACHIC:** | Promotes nutrition, tones the stomach and stimulates the appetite. |
| **TONIC:** | Invigorates and strengthens the body. |

Suggested introductory books on ECKANKAR,
the most ancient spiritual teaching in
all the universes . . .

**IN MY SOUL I AM FREE**
(Biography on Sri Paul Twitchell by Brad Steiger)

**YOUR RIGHT TO KNOW**
(Compilation of articles on contemporary subjects)

**THE TIGER'S FANG**
(An understanding of levels of heaven)

**THE FLUTE OF GOD** (Psychology of Spirit)

**THE SPIRITUAL NOTEBOOK**
(History of ECKANKAR)

**STRANGER BY THE RIVER**
(Love and wisdom of the ages)

**LETTERS TO GAIL, VOLS. I & II**
(Basic text)

**FROM HEAVEN TO THE PRAIRIE**
(Biography of Sri Darwin Gross)

**THE WIND OF CHANGE**
(Humorous recollections of Sri Harold Klemp)

Books on ECKANKAR can be found or ordered at your
local bookstore.

In many areas around the world, discussion classes on the
introductory books of ECKANKAR are being held, which
the public is welcome to attend. ECKANKAR Centers will
be listed in the local telephone book. For a free book catalog,
more information on ECKANKAR and/or ECKANKAR
activities, please write to:

**ECKANKAR**
**P.O. Box 3100**
**Menlo Park, California 94025**
**U.S.A.**

*(detach here)*

213